NO MORE LOVING

Patricia Robins

CHIVERS

British Library Cataloguing in Publication Data available

This Large Print edition published by BBC Audiobooks Ltd, Bath, 2010.
Published by arrangement with the Author.

U.K. Hardcover ISBN 978 1 408 45740 5
U.K. Softcover ISBN 978 1 408 45741 2

C460474295

Printed and bound in Great Britain by
CPI Antony Rowe, Chippenham and Eastbourne

CHAPTER ONE

She sat beside him in the tourist cabin of the Comet and thought:

What am I doing here? Why did I come? I wish I never had!

But at that moment, as if reading her thoughts, he took her hand and squeezed it tightly between his own. She turned her head to meet his gaze and he smiled at her.

'It's so marvellous to be with you!' he said in a low voice.

On her other side was an elderly woman, unmarried. Kerry had already spoken a few words to her in the Departure lounge and discovered that she was a school mistress travelling to Florence on a week's sight-seeing tour. Kerry wondered if the woman had noticed Steve holding her hand; if she thought they were honeymooners. Then Steve said:

'I had a terrible feeling you wouldn't turn up at the last minute. Couldn't really believe it would all come off until I actually saw you at the airport. I love you, Kerry!'

'If we were alone, he would kiss me now,' she thought. 'Why don't I feel in the same lover-like mood?' Then her thoughts switched to what he had just said. Was it telepathy that had prompted his fears that she mightn't turn up? Had he sensed her odd reluctance to be here?

'Love me just a little bit?'

His eyes were smiling. She nodded, uncertain if it were true. Did she love him? How could one gauge love? *What* was love?

His voice was very low now. He whispered:

'I wish we were in bed! God, how I want you . . .'

Bed! Was that all men could think of? Bed, sex; sex, bed. But that wasn't altogether fair. She, too, wanted sex and preferably in a bed. She had hated the squalid love-making in the back of Steve's Jag; hated the hurried, uncomfortable fumbling and heavy breathing. They both disliked it. That was why they had planned this week abroad together—so as to be free, able to have all the sex they wanted—and *in bed.*

Her mouth tightened. She withdrew her fingers from Steve's. In order not to hurt his feelings, she occupied both hands with the lighting of a cigarette she did not really want.

'I must snap out of this!' she told herself sharply.

It was unfair to Steve—unfair to both of them. She loved him—they loved each other. That was why they had come away together. Sex was the ultimate and natural way of expressing love. Why sneer at it? But it did not always spring from love. No—not always, argued a voice inside her.

The first time she had slept with Steve had

2

been out of pity. Years ago, before she had married Luke, Steve had been madly in love with her. Because then she had only eyes for Luke, she hadn't even looked at Steve. Luke had been all that mattered in her life—handsome, amusing, attractive Luke. By comparison Steve was commonplace, unremarkable except for the faithful unrelenting adoration that he showered on her unwillingly and which she so often accepted.

Poor Steve! He'd never married—never wanted anyone but her. For seven years he'd stayed in love with her. Sometimes his very fidelity irritated her. When her marriage to Luke began to go on the rocks, Steve had reappeared, still faithful, still wanting her. And because she was as important to him as ever, he soon noticed her unhappiness, the thinness of her miserable face and soon he wormed the truth out of her. Luke had been unfaithful—not just once but over and over again. He couldn't say 'no' to a pretty face and slowly but surely these casual promiscuous affairs broke Kerry's heart.

Do hearts break? she asked herself, now. Or is it just one's spirit, one's pride, one's vanity? Maybe Luke only destroyed my faith in love and men—my will to make my marriage work; my determination to make him into a real husband.

Steve had tried to help; tried to comfort and restore her morale. At first, his attentions had seemed impersonal, therefore acceptable. But one night when she had dissolved into tears of self-pity, his comforting arms had become no longer those of just a friend. He lost control of himself and covered her wet face with desperate, passionate kisses. He had said:

'Oh, my God, Kerry—how unfair life can be! You say Luke doesn't want you and here am I—I want you so much I could die of it . . .'

So why not let him have what mattered so much to him and so little to Luke. Her body meant a priceless gift to Steve; to Luke it seemed nothing—poor in comparison with that of his newest cheap little girl friend. Steve had been faithful without reward for ten years. Luke hadn't been faithful for ten months! Why should Luke win?

So that had been the first time and it had meant nothing to Kerry beyond the gift of a kindness, a favour to Steve. Inevitably, there followed other times, other moments of pity and gradually Steve's passionate need of her became in a curious way like a necessary drug for her pain, her bitterness. Luke's defections were somehow softened by Steve's increasing need of her. She was always strictly honest with Steve. He'd known that if Luke so much as crooked his little finger, Kerry would drop him like a stone. He'd known how much she still loved her husband, useless, worthless, shallow though he was. It did not stop Steve from trying.

'Leave him. Marry me. I love you. I don't care if you aren't in love with me. All I ask is the chance to go on loving you, possessing you. Kerry, I want you, I want you so much.'

But she wouldn't leave Luke. Nor would she risk Luke's finding out that she had in her turn, been unfaithful to him. If Luke knew, *he* might divorce *her.* Somewhere deep in the recesses of her heart, she still hoped he would tire of these cheap-scented, giggling little girl friends who seemed to attract him, and return to his wife. It wasn't that she was not attractive. She was considered beautiful not only by Steve but by many men. She had a good figure—fine eyes—a lovely skin and mouth. She dressed well. She was amusing. But for Luke this was not enough. He had grown tired of her. He needed something new to explore. He was the born hunter. It was the first spoils of the chase that intrigued him.

Nothing was going to change Luke. She was no longer even sure if she cared whether he changed. While she *had* cared, she had fought him tooth and nail; battled against every new mistress—with the same desperate urgency. She had begged him, pleaded with him. She had had no pride, Luke had left her none when he openly and shamelessly admitted to his affairs.

'If you don't like my girl friends why the hell do you stay with me?' once he had asked her.

She had stared unbelievingly at him. So

handsome—so spoiled—so shameless.

'Luke, I love you. Surely you don't *have* to behave like this? It isn't as though I've been frigid—I've never refused to make love when you wanted me, Luke. I've wanted it too. Luke, please. It's so—so pointless!'

He'd looked down at her with his brazen, impudent smile, even patting her cheek—charming as ever, quite lover-like, yet obviously sick of her—just for the moment while he had a new toy to amuse him.

'I've told you these girls don't mean anything—I'm not in love with them. Why do you have to make such a scene? If you could only stop being so possessive—so jealous, we'd get along all right . . .'

'Luke, I'm your wife!'

'And whose fault is that? You were the one who wanted so much to get married. You were the one who said you couldn't stand having an affair. You were the one who wanted a marriage certificate and security. Well, now you've got what you wanted and you're not satisfied. I warned you I wasn't the type for domestic bliss. It bores me. You're a lovely girl—lovelier than many of these girls I go about with. But I know you too well. There's nothing left for me to discover. But if we were not married it would still have some piquancy for me.'

It was all too true. Luke would have been content if she had remained his mistress. He

6

loathed being tied. It did something to him, made him go cold on her. But then Luke had never loved her the way she had loved him . . . with depth—with fidelity.

Maybe in every man–woman relationship, there had to be one who loved more than the other. Maybe this was equally true about her relationship with Steve. *He* was the one who really loved—and in a way she was just using him as Luke used her, his wife. But only in a way . . . in the last year she had grown deeply attached to him. She needed him. It was different from the passionate total love that she'd given Luke. It was a more critical kind of affection, a withdrawn appraisal of Steve's kind, generous nature; of his worth. Her head ruled her heart now. She accepted the truth—the fact that here, with Steve, lay a happiness she could never have found with the man she had married. Only her heartstrings pulled her back. She was still conscious of her own compulsive, possessive need for the man she had married and who repeatedly betrayed her.

Maybe that was why she felt this need now to fight against Steve's need for sexual possession. She didn't want him to want her *that* way. She wanted him to love her; not just her body as Luke did. At the same time she knew that the two were in some peculiar way, inseparable. Whenever Steve felt particularly loving, he also experienced the need to express his love physically. The one fired the other.

7

That was right and normal and yet still she resisted him.

Steve did not understand this contradiction. He expected Kerry to feel the same physical demands.

'If you loved me, you'd want me the moment we met—the way I want you. Just to look at you coming towards me with that half smile on your face is enough . . . but you . . .'

He broke off, shrugging his shoulders helplessly.

She tried to explain that she *wanted* him to want her but more even than that, she wanted him to love her. Until she could be reassured about the mental side, she wasn't all that interested in passion. She almost suspected it.

'But it isn't something you can switch on and off!' Steve argued. It's a kind of instantaneous triggering-off. I see you . . . I want you. No other woman has ever made me feel that way consistently. It's because I love you, Kerry—honestly.'

She tried to remember if she had ever felt that way about Luke and knew she had. There were times when she would look across a room and wish they were alone and in bed . . . wish he would come close to her even if it were just to take her hand. She had been instantly and lastingly attracted to him and during the brief six months when they had lived together—still unmarried—they had never seemed able to have enough of each other. But after their

8

wedding Luke's desire for her body seemed to grow less. At first she had not noticed—then, when she did realize he no longer kissed her very often; seldom sat deliberately close to her or touched her hand or cheek or blazed suddenly into desire for her, she had accepted it as a normal process of time. She told herself firmly that no two people could continuously live at a wild pace. And she didn't even want it to be like that herself. She ought to be able to share a room with Luke without actually sleeping with him. Yet deep down inside she began to fear Luke was growing tired of her, she even began to feel she would be glad to put their relationship on a more intellectual plane—be excellent friends rather than passionate lovers.

But the eventual discovery that Luke was being unfaithful reignited her own passionate need of him. She had tried to step on those feelings ruthlessly—too proud to show Luke that she wanted him despite the fact that he had another girl in his life, and totally unable to accept the knowledge that she must share him. There had been long, lonely nights when she had had to fight hard with herself not to step over the few feet of carpet from her bed into his; not to throw herself into his arms and make him want her more than he wanted that other, newer love.

Kerry tore her thoughts away from the past and all the bitter humiliations. It didn't matter

9

any more—it *was* past. Now she was here with Steve; on her way to Italy and he loved her, truly and honestly as Luke had never done, with an integrity that Luke lacked.

Gratefully, she slipped her hand back in his. Steve gave her a pleased smile.

'Happy?' he asked tenderly.

She nodded. It would be so easy to be happy with Steve if she could only forget Luke and the past and live in the present. For one whole week she must not think of home or her flat, or the long, dreary, heartbreaking months that would succeed *this* week. She must not allow herself to think of or wonder if Luke was taking advantage of her absence in order to bring his latest girl back into her home . . . into their bed . . .

'Could we have a drink?' she asked Steve quickly. 'I'm thirsty.'

Steve beckoned to the steward. A few minutes later she was drinking Dubonnet with bitter lemon and Steve was lifting his glass to touch hers.

'To us and our holiday!' he said, looking into her eyes.

*   *   *

He wanted her so much it was like a bad attack of indigestion—only worse because there was nothing he could take to relieve the pain except having her. He glanced at his watch and

10

saw that there was still another half hour to go before they landed at Milan. Then there was the long drive down to Florence—hours before they would be alone in the hotel . . .

He looked away from her eyes in which he could see his own reflection. They were such a deep, smoky blue. Like the colour of a Kerry Blue—hence the nickname which her father had given her as a little girl. Her real name was Katriona but no one ever called her that, reflected Steve, except that phoney artist husband of hers.

At the thought of Luke anger hit Steve a hard blow in the midriff—so sudden and strong that it replaced the ache of desire. If there were one man in the world he despised and disliked, it was Luke Austin. How could Kerry ever have loved such a bastard of a fellow.

Steve leant back in his chair and stared out into the billowing mass of cloud through which the plane was now passing. With a sigh he realized that he was just covering the same old ground of why, why, *why!*

He supposed that Kerry's husband was handsome—or might seem so to women. He had dark, almost Italian good looks. Women were odd creatures—they seemed to like the long Byronic hair, big curving mouth, deep sunken brilliant eyes. But to Steve—a healthy sports type—Luke was a beatnik, slovenly in his clothes, tie always crooked—like his

11

crooked attractive smile. Perhaps a woman felt a maternal desire to keep such a fellow in order! Though *maternal* was scarcely the word to describe the type of female Luke Austin attracted! The hard, gay, glittering butterfly sort of blonde, or the sensuous red-head. The only time Luke had shown good taste was when he chose Kerry—fair, slender, graceful Kerry with her exquisite long throat and slim cool hands.

Steve wondered, not for the first time, if he was getting old in his ideas. Kerry had once told him he was 'conventional' which could be the reason why he felt a deep-rooted objection to the type of man she had married. It was true that his life had followed a conventional pattern. His parents were middle-class, fairly well off, his father retired from the regular army. He had been sent to a good prep school and then to Marlborough. Lacking any particular academic ability he had not gone to University but had started work in the small market town in Sussex where his parents then lived, in an estate agency.

His reliable, steady application to his work had led eventually to a partnership and this last year they had been able to open two new branches in neighbouring towns. He wasn't exactly rich but comfortably off and could well afford to marry—the only trouble being that he couldn't forget Kerry or stop loving her. If he couldn't marry her, he preferred to stay single.

Now that Kerry was a married woman, she probably represented his one and only sin against propriety and the conventions. To spend a week abroad with a married woman was something he would not have dreamt of doing had circumstances been otherwise—but then everything about Kerry was exceptional and had changed his life beyond normal barriers and the standards by which he usually lived.

He glanced sideways at her. Her eyes were closed. How long the little fans of black lashes looked on the pale cheeks with the high, haunting bones. How young she looked with that fair untidy hair. She seemed to be sleeping—or lost in a dream. With a sudden stab of jealousy, he wondered whether she was thinking of her husband. There were times when he could convince himself that she disliked Luke—had 'got over' her blind adoration for him; had at last begun to love him, Steve, a little bit. But there were many more occasions when he felt that he was very very far from possessing her. Even as he actually made love to her, he had the uncomfortable feeling that he might be possessing her body but not her essential self; *that* was still chained to her artist husband.

Steve sighed. All thoughts led back to Luke Austin.

The son of a grocer, Luke might never have

entered Kerry's sphere but for his ability to produce so-called works of the impressionist school. Steve had never been able to discover what the splashes of garish paints were meant to represent but he supposed that was due to his own artistic blindness rather than Luke's lack of genius. After all, his paintings had won him a scholarship to an art school and the government had been prepared to fork out to have the young man trained. In a way, Luke had proved their faith in him, for he had become a free lance and sold enough canvases to live on a moderately comfortable scale. Young marrieds living in Hampstead near Luke's studio bought up his paintings for their modern flats; sometimes genuine critics or collectors bought one of his pictures. Kerry, anyway, believed that Luke had genius and Steve did not know enough about modern painting to agree or disagree with her. He only knew that he would not have given half a crown for one of those blurbs of colour which looked to him like the work of a four-year-old let loose with a palette of poster paints and a pot of Indian ink.

Being fair minded, Steve had tried not to be too prejudiced. He recognized that he was Luke's natural enemy because the artist had 'stolen' his girl. Perhaps Steve would have felt less biased had Luke proved that he could make Kerry happy. But he had merely made her life a wretched hell.

If only she would leave him! Perhaps, if he did not rush her too much, she would come round to divorcing Luke. Heaven knew she had evidence enough. But that wasn't really the point. The real issue was, *did Kerry want to leave Luke?* Had she really stopped loving him? And even if she had crossed both these hurdles, would she marry him, Steve?

He was sure that she had no idea how much store he was setting on their week away together. He had seven days in which to prove himself to her; to prove that he could make her happy; by the very force of his love and affection, prove that she would be far better off with him, than with her faithless artist. He had been terrified that she wouldn't come, though he had no real reason for his fear. There was no one but Luke to object and Luke would doubtless be glad to get his wife out of the way and feel more free to enjoy his latest amour.

It wasn't even as though Kerry had parents around, who might ask questions. Her mother and father had been divorced soon after the war. The former had married again—an American business man this time, and moved to the States. Kerry used to live with her father who was a dentist in Leeds, in the care of his sister. Now both father and aunt were dead. And the mother had died also, out in Chicago. Kerry had no kith or kin left. She had only Luke and a cousin, Joanna, who used to live with her in Leeds and to whom she was devoted. The two girls were more like sisters.

Joanna was some years older, a strange girl. She was a dark, plump, attractive creature, Kerry said, but Steve wondered sometimes if she was the right influence for Kerry. Joanna—Jo to her intimate friends—led a bachelor-girl life in a Chelsea flat just off the King's Road. She refused to marry although she had had many lovers. Steve sometimes suspected that they kept her. He could not approve of the life she led but there was nothing underhand or sly about Joanna. She was quite frank about what she called her 'life of sin' and she had once said to Kerry, when they were talking about Steve,

'Any time you two love-birds want to borrow this flat while I'm away, you only have to say the word.'

It wasn't so much that she deliberately sinned as that she saw no wrong in sinning. Sex to Joanna was natural, right and proper. There wasn't any harm in it—it was merely unconventional, she said—against a lot of stuffy man-made laws. Kerry's story to Luke was that she was going abroad for a week with Joanna. Steve wondered if Luke believed that or that he just did not care enough to inquire further into his wife's excuse for being away a week. Steve privately believed that he guessed but just did not care . . .

Steve felt Kerry's eyes on him. Turning he

16

looked long and deeply into those beautiful blue eyes. She blinked quickly as if pulling a veil over her thoughts, then smiled at him. His heart turned over. He reached at once for her hand.

'Penny for them, Kerry!' he said.

'Oh, I wasn't really thinking of anything much!' she answered, which shut him out of her mental world. He knew it would be useless to probe. When she was ready to tell him what went on inside that confused little brain, she would come out with it.

'I do love you so much. I suppose you get bored listening to me saying that. *Does* it bore you, darling?'

She shook her fair head, pushing back the thick mane of hair that continually fell across her eyes.

'No! I like to hear it—any woman loves to be told she is loved.'

'A man, too!' Steve said softly. 'Do you love me, Kerry? Just a little?'

She wanted to be able to say at once, 'Yes, yes, I love you a lot' but her essential cruel honesty forbade it. She could not say *'I love you'* to any man unless she was quite, quite sure it was true. This exaggerated desire to be absolutely frank had been instilled in her by her father; maybe because her mother had lied to him so often that he had developed a phobia about 'telling the truth'. Now Kerry was beginning to doubt the wisdom of *complete* honesty. Sometimes it was too brutal. Steve would be so much happier if she could pretend a little and say 'I love you' even if it were not absolutely so. Wouldn't she have suffered less if Luke had not so often brutally told her the facts?

'*I don't deny I'm sleeping with her—why should* I?' he would say as though proud of his honesty.

But Luke had no shame about the other woman. In a strange kind of way, he enjoyed the effect his confessions had on Kerry. She used to try to puzzle out how he could bring himself to hurt her so badly and finally decided that he was 'paying her back' for forcing him into a marriage he had never really wanted.

Steve tried to debunk the idea.

'He didn't have to say yes! No one can force a man into the Registrar's Office. No one stood at his back with a gun saying "*either—or*" did they? Don't say you "made" him marry you, Kerry. He could have refused.'

But she would always believe in her heart that she had more or less blackmailed Luke into the wedding by refusing to continue living with him unless he did marry her. In those days Luke had been so crazy about her; he had believed it was worth while to forgo freedom and bachelorhood for Kerry. But that was before she learned through bitter experience that each one of Luke's affairs was The Big Thing in his life; that each new mistress, before her novelty palled, was fascinating enough to make him behave as though he was really in love.

Kerry began to find out that all that Luke really knew about love was that it meant *making love,* at which he was an expert. Tenderness, unselfishness, generosity, these charming attributes were all part of the same arrow striking at a girl's heart and leading her to the bedroom. So long as he desired a woman, he could and did give her everything she wanted. It was only afterwards, when he had finished with her, that the tenderness, the friendship, the sweetness vanished and he became cruelly casual and finally indifferent. In his way he was schizophrenic. He could be the perfect lover—or the heartless cad.

Sometimes Kerry thought she had learned the lesson Luke had to teach. Other times, such as now in the aircraft with Steve, she felt that she was still learning. Part of her mind said: *'Luke has finished with you—it can never be as it was again.'* Another part argued: *'But he tires of these girls very quickly . . . one day he'll have had enough of them and will come back to me . . .'*

Deep down inside the hope was still there—despite Joanna's warnings to the contrary; despite her own common sense that made her realize that although she was Luke's legal wife, she was now little better than one of his discarded girl friends.

'For God's sake, leave him, Kerry! Marry that faithful young man of yours,' Joanna often said to her. Jolly, casual, happy-go-lucky Joanna—as faithless in her way as Luke, but less cruel.

'But I still love Luke!' To Joanna, Kerry could admit it.

Joanna sighed.

'Love! To be *in* love is to be in hell. It is better just to make love, then forget, Kerry.'

To be in hell! How right Joanna was about that. Heaven had very soon turned to hell for Kerry. Within three months of her marriage the pain and doubting and suffering had begun. Life with Luke had become unendurable. Kerry was too sensitive, too highly-strung—too dependent and gentle—to stand up to the brutal kind of indifference she received from her husband once he had stopped wanting her. Yet she could not bring herself to leave him, to give up hope that one day . . .

'Darling, are you feeling all right? You look pale!' said Steve.

'I wish we were already there!' she replied.

What she really meant was that she wanted this week of a new life to begin—to occupy her mind and thoughts so that she could forget the everyday life at home with all its problems.

'So do I, Kerry. I've booked a double room. It could be a bit awkward if they ask for passports, but I hope you won't be subjected to

20

any embarrassment . . .'

Steve went on talking, but Kerry's mind wandered away from his words to the meaning behind them. He wanted this holiday to be perfect; he was worrying in case something should happen to make her wish she had not come. She knew, as well as though she were inside his mind, that he was desperately hoping that this week together would be so wonderful that she would agree to make it a permanent state of affairs.

Part of her surrendered in gratitude. It was so lovely to have a man really care again; to feel secure and to know that she could relax and be looked after without having to make any effort herself. Yet something in Kerry bristled and put up a prickly barrier of defence against this unspoken attack on her emotions. She couldn't allow Steve to drug her senses completely and make her agree to do something she did not really want to do. She must guard against his loving, for it held some positive threat to logical thinking. If ever she agreed to leave Luke and marry Steve, it must be because she was quite sure in her mind that it was right for them both. Never, never again would she let her heart or her emotions rule her head.

'Safety belt on, darling. We're coming down.'

The plane tipped to one side and began to descend. She let Steve fasten her belt for her and stopped thinking.

CHAPTER TWO

Steve came across the room and gently removed Kerry's hands from the clasps of her suitcase. With the same gentle determination, he turned her round and bending his head, kissed her. She shut her eyes. She always shut her eyes when he kissed her; not because she did not like his face, which in fact she did; but because she was afraid of the naked desire she knew she would see there. It was only after he had made love to her that she could look at him; sure then that she would find a tender, smiling love and gratitude.

He went on kissing her and slowly, her body began to respond. But still her mind stayed free, seeing against her closed eye-lids the twin beds with their crisp white counterpanes; her half opened suitcase; the large windows with the green jalousies looking over the garden; the striped awning over the balcony on which they would have breakfast. Steve had chosen this hotel. It was really a converted villa in beautiful grounds a few kilometres outside the city of Florence. When first Kerry had seen it she had experienced a thrill of surprised pleasure. She admired the white pillars, the carved ceilings, the great cool hall with its marble floor, and white statue of a nymph holding aloft an alabaster lamp. There were palms everywhere and old gilt and crystal and ornate Italian ornaments. The dining salon opened onto a terrace shaded by a grape vine. It was not in any way the kind of place to be found in England, where a man took a girl away for a week.

'No!' she told herself sharply. 'That is a nasty way to think. Steve loves me—I think I love him, too. I want him to touch me. And he wants me . . .'

She looked up into his square, brown, thoroughly masculine face. A strong face, ugly–attractive, exuding vitality and amiability, the face of a man one could trust.

She tightened her arms around his neck and sensing her first active response, Steve's hands began to move over her body. In a little while, he undressed her and pulled back the counterpane so that she could lie down on the bed. She lay still, watching him undress and unwittingly comparing him with Luke. Steve was so much broader, stronger, more virile. He loved the out-of-doors, the sun. He was a keen golfer and tennis player, a big cheerful man. Luke was a creature of the night, pale white, soft, narrow in the shoulder and hips. Luke was slender and sensual, wildly fascinating to women and with a vitality of his own—a strength that could outrun Steve's when he chose to exert it.

She closed her eyes as Steve came towards her. She felt the weight of his body beside her,

23

then his warm hands touched her breasts. Involuntarily she shivered. At once he pulled a blanket over her but presently, she pushed it back as the fire of his body set light to hers. Soon, thought ceased and sensation became the only recognizable thing. Her own role was passive. She did not make love to Steve. He made love to her and very soon it was all over.

When they could speak, he said:

'I wanted you more than ever before, my darling. Each time it seems to get worse. I'm like a kid with his first girl. Just to look at you makes me tremble. You're so beautiful, Kerry, so very beautiful.'

He touched her small, firm breasts and ran his warm hand down her side, coming to rest at her waist. She thought:

Why doesn't Luke find me beautiful too? Then she remembered that once he, too, had found her perfect and told her so.

'I'll have to paint that Cleopatra body of yours,' he had said. But his portrait had been 'impressionist' and she had been unable to recognize even a female shape in the blur of colours he had splashed onto the canvas. She did not necessarily think the painting bad— only supposed that she, being no artist, could not see its merit. She would have preferred a true portrait—so as to see as she could see in a mirror that her body was made for love and loving; for Luke's delight.

'Do you really think me beautiful?' she

24

asked Steve curiously.

He laughed and laid his hard brown cheek against her softer one.

'In any other woman, I would call that remark sheer vanity,' he said. 'But in you, my darling, I sense a real desire to know the truth. Well, the truth is, my love, that you drive me to distraction. I can't sit within yards of you without desiring you; longing to touch, to feel, to hold, to kiss, to possess. If you ask me to explain what your particular attraction is for me, I couldn't. I have often asked myself what it is about you that is different from *other* women. I suppose there are others with firm pointed breasts just as delightful—with tiny waists, with rounded hips and long, slender legs like yours. But they haven't your dreamy, smoky blue eyes, your strange little-girl smile, your vulnerable mouth with that fascinating curve to it. Maybe it is your face, Kerry. Or maybe it is just the *"you"* in you! Maybe it is nothing more than that I love you quite terribly.'

She turned quickly and kissed his mouth. There were two Kerrys behind that kiss; one who was grateful and warmly satisfied by Steve's words and love; the other who still held back from giving the right reply to his eternal question 'Do you love me?' Now she should be answering, 'Yes—yes, Steve, I do, very much!' But she stayed silent.

The kiss, however, satisfied him. He smiled

25

and said softly:

'This is like having a dream come true, being here quite alone with you and knowing we have a whole week ahead of us. I've thought of nothing else. I've even found it impossible to concentrate on my work. Everything I do relates indirectly to you. Do you know, a few days ago I was asked by a client to let a cottage under the Sussex Downs for six months. All I could think of was renting it so that you and I could have somewhere to go where we could be alone together! To tell you the truth, Kerry, I still haven't put out particulars of that cottage. I thought maybe you might like the idea of it as a bolt-hole for us. What do you think, darling? I could easily afford it.'

She shook her head.

'No, Steve, I don't think I'd want that. I know what I'm saying is contrary to the way I am now behaving and have behaved. I go out for an evening with you—we find some place where we can be alone and we make love. But that isn't what I want either. I don't think I want to make any definite plans until I can rearrange my whole life. Oh, I admit I'm prevaricating. But I don't want a sordid hole-in-the-corner affair with you, and I don't yet know if I mean to leave Luke and marry you. Until I *am* sure I cannot commit myself to anything. Does that sound very selfish?'

He began to stroke her hair. He avoided the

26

entreaty in her eyes.

'No, you're absolutely honest, as usual, and it's best that way. It's just that sometimes I don't really understand you, darling. I mean, it is all over between you and Luke, isn't it? It must be!'

She nodded, biting nervously on her lower lip.

'Then what's the use of waiting? What are you waiting *for*? I can understand you not being sure whether you really love me or not; or if you want to marry me. But what I don't understand is how you can go on living with Luke, allowing yourself to be humiliated by him; cooking and keeping house for him—in short, acting as his wife and yet not being a real wife to him, while he behaves like a . . . Sorry!' Steve added quickly, carried away by his savage hatred of Kerry's husband.

She thought:

Now is the time I should tell Steve that I don't know whether or not I am still in love with Luke. But he just wouldn't understand. He thinks I am proud. He wouldn't understand how I can endure the humiliation and insecurity of my life.

She said:

'Please don't rush me, Steve. I know it's hard on you but I can't yet see the wood for the trees. At least, I'll say this—if I ever marry again it will be you—that is if you still want to marry me when the time comes.'

'Want to!' Steve exclaimed and kissed her quickly and hard on the mouth. 'I shall want you, Kerry, any way, any time—with or without marriage. Preferably with. I want to feel that you belong to me as my wife; to know that we can just pack up and come away together like this with no one to say us nay; to know that when I knock off work at the end of each day, I shall come home and find *you* waiting for me; to know that I could come home at any time of day, want you and be able to take you up to our bedroom and love you and love you, my darling, adorable Kerry.'

His sincere adoration for her—his boyish exuberance and enthusiasm touched her deeply. She traced the line of his eyebrows. Her lips were sad, her eyes thoughtful.

'Suppose I got ill—had an awful accident—anything. Suppose I couldn't make love, Steve—ever again? What then?'

He smiled at her.

'Suppose!' he echoed, imitating her voice. 'I don't WANT to suppose anything so ghastly. You have too many morbid thoughts, my love. It's far nicer to suppose that we are now married and that it's lunch time, and I've come home unexpectedly, and you tell me you haven't anything in the house to eat. So I take you to bed and make a meal of you instead.'

On another occasion that might have amused her. Today she felt too strained and on edge. She did not return his smile. She gave a fretful toss of her head and said:

'I'm being serious. Suppose what I said *happened.* Would you still want me for the rest of your life?'

The teasing smile left his face. He caught her in his arms and spoke to her in a changed voice—a slightly angry voice.

'Look here. Nothing in the whole wide world could stop me wanting you, Kerry. I've loved you for God knows how long and I've no doubt in my mind that I'll go on loving you till we're both dead. I can imagine it might be hell living with you if you were unable to make love. Yet that would seem better to me than living without you. Don't you understand, darling, that I love you, *I love you.*'

She was nearly crying. She said:

'But Steve, what is love? I looked it up in a dictionary only last week and it said: *fondness.* I'm fond of Joanna. I was fond of my father and my Aunt Maggie. It said, too: *an affection of the mind caused by that which delights.* Well, that could be a picture, an object, *a thing.* It said love could mean: *a devoted attachment to one of the opposite sex.* Okay, but don't you see, Steve, that means physical attraction. I want it to be something much more. It doesn't seem easy to define and yet I long to know what the true meaning is. Not just a dry answer in a dictionary compiled by a stick of a professor.'

'Look, my darling,' Steve said after a pause. 'I am sure that what I feel for you is love—love as you wish it to be. But I don't always know how to express it. You would probably say that what I feel is sheer passion. So it is at times. But not all the time.'

Kerry sat up, tucking her legs beneath her. She looked down at Steve intently.

'Try to define love, in more detail. Just to please me. It doesn't matter if you don't succeed. But try!'

He shrugged and said:

'Funny One, love is lots and lots of things, particles that go to make up a whole. It's everything your dictionary says and more. For me, other women don't really exist. I can see that they are attractive but I can't feel attracted by them because your body only has the power to stir mine—as soon as I touch it—or see it. It means that whilst I can exert all my will power to put you out of my mind, your image stays with me, haunting me like a persistent little ghost. It means that anything I do has no point to it unless it leads ultimately to you or is in some devious way, *for* you. I can work with a will if I can make myself believe that one day, the money I'm accumulating will eventually be spent on you. I can get up each morning, delighting in a new day only if that day promises to include you or brings me a letter or a phone call from you. An ordinary dull wet cold miserable day can become magical in an instant if you suddenly let me know that we can meet. Alternatively, a beautiful summer morning can become the most wretched day of the year if I find you can't meet me after all. I am utterly dependent upon you and yet I want more than anything for *you* to depend on *me*. I want to be part of you and for you to be part of me. I want to make you mine and yet I never want to change one tiny part of the Kerry that you are now— which is perfect. I know that if you grow old and grey and lose some of that youthful loveliness, as no doubt one day you must, you will still seem beautiful and desirable to me, even when I have lost the capacity to desire you physically. My mind will continue to adore and need you. It's strange, Kerry, that my love is so real a thing to me, yet you cannot understand what I feel!'

She was silent. Steve's description of love touched her profoundly. But it differed to a large degree from the love she felt for Luke. Steve's experiences were joyous and beautiful. There was so little joy in the years she shared with Luke. They were full of pain and anguish, both mental and physical. Sometimes ugly, searing years that withered her heart.

A sense of acute inferiority overcame her. Perhaps there was some quality lacking in her. Whatever she had given Luke—and she could never give more of herself to any other man— it was insufficient to keep him at her side. Why should Steve not get sick of her once he was her husband and constant familiarity took the gilt off the thrill of possession. Wasn't it because he couldn't really possess her now that he was so mad to do so?

She looked at Steve with a mixture of anxiety and mistrust. It was always all so easy at first—it had been the same when she and Luke had become lovers; the thrill of possession, of belonging, of being needed and necessary to the other. But at the end of the week would Steve still be such a devoted lover? Or would he, too, grow casual? Take her just the smallest bit for granted? Cease to let the light of his love, his affection, revolve around her so brightly? Didn't all men want most the woman who was hard to get?

He reached up and pulled her down beside him.

'You're too far away from me up there!' he said smiling. 'I need you close, dearest.'

It was as if he had sensed her mental withdrawal and needed the reassurance of physical contact with her. She sank back into his arms, torn by her doubts and griefs. He was less troubled.

He is like a child! she thought. He has to touch and see in order to feel secure. I know he loves me—but the moment he is out of my sight, away from me—I begin to wonder, to doubt again . . .

'Kerry, darling! Don't fade away from me. You are thinking about something important to you—I can read your face. Can't you share your thoughts with me? Don't shut me out!'

She buried her face against his neck. How well she knew his feeling of being shut out. Snatches from the past flashed across her mind. Luke, in his studio, in paint-stained slacks and check shirt, paint brush in one hand—cigarette between his lips—turning to her with something like dislike in his narrow brilliant mocking eyes—saying: 'Must you bother me now? Can't you see I'm busy!'

Luke, in bed, yawning, dark dishevelled hair across his eyes—muttering: 'Do you have to talk half the night? I'm tired. Do let me go to sleep, damn you!'

Luke, hurriedly thrusting a letter back into its envelope.

'This? It's nothing—just a bill for canvases.'

Luke twisting away from her touch, her timid beseeching touch, grunting at her: 'Lay off me, for Christ's sake. I've other things to do.'

A deep red flush crept into Kerry's cheeks. The memory of humiliation, of despairing loneliness made her feel sick. Never, never again could she offer her love freely to any man.

This affair with Steve was only possible because he gave her all his passion and affection unreservedly, spontaneously, without asking any reward save that she should stay near him.

She heard his tender, persuasive voice.

33

'Want to go out this evening, darling? Or shall we dine here and have an early night. Then tomorrow we can do some sight-seeing and find somewhere to go in the evening.'

'Let's stay here!' Kerry agreed. She was suddenly conscious of tiredness—of a deep ache that was pure fatigue. She knew she ought not to be tired—the flight had been comfortable and relaxing; the drive down from Milan equally comfortable and restful. The tiredness came from her mind. If only I could stop thinking, analysing, just enjoy myself! she thought.

Tensions were bad and she lived on a taut wire of stretched nerves that slackened only when she slept. (Or when Steve made love to her.)

Oh, God! she thought miserably. Am I making use of my poor old Steve? Using him like a drug—to drown my memories of Luke and the stinking mess he's made of our marriage?

She resolved to be particularly sweet to Steve. It wasn't difficult. She cast off depression and suddenly became uninhibited—the radiant joyous Kerry who had entranced Steve when he first met her. Pain and sorrow had carved lines around those wonderful smoky eyes; saddened the delicately cut lips; etched a few lines, too, across the marble of her forehead with those narrow, straight brows and silken, heavy eyelashes. But this evening

34

she seemed transformed—she literally danced, he thought, watching her, fascinated; danced around the room, stopping to touch its treasures—remarking on the beauty of the carved gilded mirror over the mantelpiece, with the cupids cresting it. On the attractive blue-satin covers of the satinwood high-backed chairs; of the silky, flowered curtains and thick white rugs on the polished floor; the cedar-wood cupboard for their clothes.

It was a wonderful, wonderful world of sun and radiant skies and a vista of distant steeples of the churches of Florence. The faint sound of the bells that never seemed to stop ringing reached them. The rich odour of damp earth below their balcony where an old Sicilian gardener was spraying the fabulous beds of scarlet carnations, wafted up to their room.

This was a glorious world—made for love and lovers. She was going to try and surrender herself, that unhappy, agonized self too often imprisoned in her glowing, ardent body, to Steve—yes—she would live for him this one week. Just for him.

They made love again before they bathed and dressed. Still sparkling, still full of good intentions, still determined to bury the thought of Luke so deep that it could not be resuscitated, Kerry gave Steve her hand. Like that they went down together to the dining salon.

More beauty here—in richly panelled walls;

great marble fireplace, wrought-iron screen; long tables laid with colourful, tempting dishes. And a young man playing a piano softly, in the light of three tall candles burning with spears, up towards the high fluted ceiling.

Steve liked good food. (Luke would be satisfied with a sausage or ham sandwich if he was painting.) Steve chose carefully for Kerry. *Truite au Bleu* . . . fillet steaks with mushrooms . . . a special Italian soufflé with Kirsch. A light white wine, and later with the excellent strong black coffee, Kerry's favourite liqueur, *Crème de Menthe frappé*.

They drank the coffee and liqueurs while they smoked their cigarettes at the little table out on the terrace, overlooking the river. The calm, cool, dark river flowed between green-fringed banks towards the beautiful Florentine bridges.

As Kerry looked up at a full moon that seemed to be hanging in the blue velvet of the sky, and at the millions of brilliant stars, she gave a little satisfied sigh.

'It is all perfect—truly romantic, Steve darling.'

He was so proud of her—of the looks that followed her as she walked from the villa. She looked very English in her cream coloured sheath dress, worn with a high choker of gold beads. There were gold bracelets on her arms; her fair hair was combed high; her smoke-blue eyes were more beautiful, he thought, than that night-blue Italian sky. He loved and desired her. And he thought that for once she, too, loved him and looked with the same desire into his eyes; that all the bells in Florence rang only for them, this night; all the stars shone in her eyes as she smiled at him.

'It's so marvellous being here with you like this, darling!' he said huskily. 'I still feel as if I'm in a dream, and it isn't true.'

But suddenly she thought of Luke and terribly her world of dreams shattered again. She thought of moments like this shared with him on their honeymoon in Paris. Her love had burned inside her like a flame, lighting up each tiny incident with a radiant, golden glow of happiness. And he had burned for her. Not the cold, sardonic Luke she had left in the studio, but a lover, like Steve, yet so different. He had taken it for granted she was passionately in love with him and did not question her feelings. And as if she was the slave of love in those days she was content to adore—to wait on him—spoil him—believe his way of life and love was right.

'Will it always be like this?' she had asked him once. He had smiled. He was sketching her head at the time, a cigarette hanging loosely from his lower lip—ash on his jacket—the artist, coldly perceptive and casual and yet crazy about her then—about all of her.

'This will last for ever,' he told her. Cynical now, she realized that it had only been for two or three months. That must have seemed quite a long time to Luke. Three months before he had needed another girl friend—a change—a new stimulus. Not that she had realized then that he was being unfaithful to her. It had taken her almost a year to understand the reason why his passion for her had cooled.

'Kerry, darling! Don't keep running away from me!'

She recovered herself quickly and looked up into Steve's anxious eyes. She wanted to stay with him. It hurt too desperately to be dragged back to the agony of the past with Luke.

'Let's go somewhere and dance, could we? I'm suddenly not tired any more,' she said.

Dancing was something she always enjoyed with Steve because it was something she had never done with Luke. He had never been able or willing to dance well. The Twist and the Maddison had bored him. He derided those who danced them. But Steve had been a good ballroom dancer. He used to take Kerry to dances before she met and married Luke.

Within minutes, Steve had ordered a taxi to take them into Florence. Kerry fetched a loose, silky coat and slipped it on, feeling suddenly cold. Once in the car it no longer seemed to her such a good idea to be going out. But Steve was enthusiastic. In halting Italian, he discovered from the driver that there was a night club near the Ponte Vecchio. He told the man:

'No tourist club, you understand? Italian people, Italian band!'

The club they were taken to was small and rather shabby but the lighting was so poor they could only see dimly. There were candles on the table. A waiter pointed proudly to the huge plateglass windows right along one of the walls. Below them ran the river. It was as though they were on the river. Kerry gave an exclamation of delight.

'How lovely!' she said, and her eyes were shining. Again the ghost of Luke receded.

The four-piece band in blue jeans and shirts, young Florentines, suddenly swung into a popular tune. A tiny slim girl in a skin-tight gold lamé dress came dancing across the room singing. The band leader sang with her and then the other musicians joined in. Soon they were all singing, laughing, enjoying themselves. Looking round the room, Kerry saw that everyone seemed to be happy and the atmosphere was convivial, friendly and romantic.

'Fun, eh?' Steve said, taking Kerry's hand.

The girl in the lamé dress walked back to the bar at the far end of the room. The band played a more sentimental tune. Couples began dancing. Kerry watched through half-shut eyes. They all danced very close to one another, oblivious to anyone else in the room. Steve took her hand and they joined the others. He held her tightly against him and she

39

felt his face against her hair. She shut her eyes—allowing sensation to replace thought. The whole atmosphere was romantic. It was so easy to let go—allow oneself to drift without thought or reason into a dream world of music, of tantalizing rhythm and sensuous delight.

'Happy?' Steve asked her.

'Yes, very!' she whispered back. His lips brushed her forehead. She felt him trembling and understood his desire. This darkness, the haunting music, the close proximity, were all designed to heighten the emotions.

Presently Steve led her back to their table. Still holding her hand he turned her gently round to look out at the water moving below them. The dark, starlit, glittering Arno, the fairy-tale shadowed splendour of the age-old bridge.

'I suppose this dive is really rather a cheap and sordid one!' observed Steve, lighting two cigarettes and giving Kerry one. 'Yet I like it here with you tremendously. It's all a question of who one is with. With the wrong person it could be ghastly. With you—the one right person for me—it's immensely enjoyable. Sex is like that, isn't it, Kerry? Ugly without love. Beautiful—when the mind and heart are involved.'

She turned to him, her face suddenly pale and emotional.

'Don't stop loving me, Steve!' she begged.

It was as though she desperately needed the pure unselfish goodness of Steve's loving. The white pages of the past years with Luke had been so defiled by him that it seemed now as if he had opened a filthy book and forced her to read it. Luke's love had turned out to be physical and paltry, without stability. An animal need, which men call infatuation. But Steve's love was a poem—a splendid shining torch in the tragic darkness. Why must she still want Luke? Whatever he had done, nothing could wipe out the force of her own feelings for him. She knew suddenly that she would never be able to love anyone with the same blind surrender. She had ceased to be herself and voluntarily become a part of Luke.

I've sold my soul to the devil! she thought, with bitter irony. And with the idea came a terrible, haunting fear. She might never be able to love again; never give herself to a man like Steve—Steve the torch bearer—the 'parfait Knight'. She was destined to spend the rest of her life on the dark fringe, outside the core of life and to join the restless, mad, lost circle that they called in this country 'La Dolce Vita'.

Tears filled her eyes. She trembled. She caught Steve's hand and hung on to it. It became a life-line, a last hope. Perhaps, after all, he could lead her back to happiness. She must stop trying to fight him; let him go his own way in bringing her close to the stars again. She didn't want to be alone in Luke's horrible darkness. Steve was trying so hard to reach her; if she could only bring down the final shutters between Luke and herself.

'Steve, I need you!' she said with a sudden violence. 'Don't leave me. Promise you'll never leave me. No matter what I say or do, don't leave me!'

He did not understand but seeing her tears he was deeply moved and yet glad. They seemed to make her more wholly his—more dependent on him.

'You're tired, my love. I'm going to take you home.'

Home! In the taxi she relaxed against him, her eyes closed, her body absorbing the warmth of his. *'Home's the place where your heart is,'* the song said. If only, Kerry thought, if only I still had a heart. But the bedroom in the beautiful villa was not yet—home. She still felt the guilt of her own infidelity to Luke outweighing all the burden of his multiple sins against their marriage. *Home* was still that studio—with Luke in it.

It was a devastating thought.

CHAPTER THREE

Steve put his hat down on a chair beside him. Now that he was actually face to face with

Kerry's cousin Joanna Heyler, he felt a little awkward although the warm and friendly smile which she had given him when she opened the door of her flat to him had relieved some of his anxiety. Why should he have been anxious? Only because of Joanna's reputation. He would have felt deeply embarrassed if she had been coy with him—too forthcoming. But she was neither and she obviously knew how to put a man at his ease. She was ready with drinks for him. The gin and French, and ice-bucket all there waiting, plus a box full of cigarettes.

'It was good of you to see me,' he said as he sat down opposite her.

'I seldom refuse to see an attractive man,' she said.

But even now her voice was friendly and her eyes mischievous, rather than coquettish. Steve relaxed.

'I'm sorry you couldn't come out and lunch with me.'

'So am I, but I had a firm date so I thought we'd just have this quick drink and a chat.'

'I've got my car outside. I can give you a lift to wherever you're finally going.'

'Thanks, but I shan't need it. I've got my own little Mini. Believe it or not as you like! Diamonds may be the best friend of some girls. Mini is mine!'

She chuckled.

She must have a lot of friends, Steve thought. He could understand now why Kerry was so fond of Joanna. She was a good deal older—six or seven years perhaps. She had long been burning the candle at both ends, and she might, Steve decided, have been Kerry's aunt rather than her cousin. She was plump, but her figure, although full, was firm and rather voluptuous. She wore a tight and low-cut dress of black linen with a wide, white belt which made her waist look bigger than it should. Four rows of white and gold beads encircled her full creamy neck. There were huge white and gold earrings dangling from her ears. And she wore slanting sunglasses with black and gold rims. They gave her an amusing look. She had, he thought, an amusing face altogether, with a hint of a double chin and dimples in her cheeks when she smiled. A 'Baby-face' some people would call it. The eyes were round and blue with sticky black lashes; the hair obviously an artificial red, back-combed into an enormous sort of cap, made her look a little top-heavy because she was short. Several bracelets jangled as she lifted her own cocktail glass to her large pink mouth. She used very strong perfume. Her best points were her beautiful and quite slim legs.

Steve decided that her success lay in her essential femininity; almost a maternal quality; and what with her deep husky voice, she was the sort of woman who, in her mid-thirties, offered men a positive wealth of sympathy,

44

understanding and—Steve imagined—love. Frank, sensual love. He could well understand a tired head being laid gratefully on that large luscious bosom. At once he liked Joanna. And later he liked her still more because she so obviously adored Kerry.

She waved a plump dimpled hand, flashing with rings (Joanna had good jewellery) around the sitting-room which was packed with furniture, full of sunlight, with scarlet curtains and cushions and masses of photographs of men, Steve noticed—all inscribed to their dearest Joanna.

'My little love-nest isn't much to look at, I'm afraid,' she said with her deep throaty laugh. 'But it's cosy, eh?'

'Very cosy,' he smiled back. 'Kerry's told me about it.'

'Oh, she often stays the night with me here, but only when that bastard of a husband of hers is away and she needs a bit of peace and quiet. My most peaceful nights are all spent with sweet Kerry. When I'm alone, if you know what I mean, we're a bit noisy up here, what with my records—' she pointed to a pile of discs—all pop numbers—on a table beside the record-player. 'And a bit of a dance—when I roll up these rugs, I generally manage to get a small party going.'

Steve bet that she did. Joanna would get anything or anyone 'going'. She exuded warmth, vitality and fun. Now he began to understand why the boys trooped in here to see her and confide in her and why she preferred not to be tied in matrimony to a domestic life. She was not a greedy self-seeking playgirl. She was the sort who would grow into a real 'Momma' who, until she died, would cradle some tired frustrated man in her warm generous arms.

He lit a cigarette and then Joanna said:

'Well—let's have it, Steve. I may call you that I hope. I've heard so much of you from Kerry and I must say I like what I see. She says you're a dear and that's what you look.'

And her big round eyes approved of the tall man, browned by the Italian sun, solid and thoroughly masculine as Kerry had always described him, the faithful ugly-attractive Steve.

'You've guessed that I've come to talk about Kerry.'

'I'm dead sure you have.'

'I'm terribly worried, Miss Heyler.'

'Listen, Baby,' she broke in, 'nobody calls me anything but Joanna, or Jo, if you prefer it.'

'Jo suits you,' he said smiling.

'Come on—what's wrong with our Kerry now? She's been through so much with that bloody-awful husband of hers I wonder if anything else *can* go wrong.'

'I wonder, too,' said Steve, leaning forward and locking his hands over his knees. 'You know we've just come back from Italy. Well, it was all heaven for me and I hoped it was for Kerry, too. She was a bundle of nerves when we got to Florence but she soon relaxed and for the whole of the rest of the week she seemed to enjoy every moment. I thought it was a wild success.'

'And wasn't it?'

'I don't know,' he said gloomily. 'I've loved that girl a long time but *you've* known her all your life and maybe you can explain what makes her tick better than I can.'

Joanna's face grew a little grave. She shrugged her plump shoulders.

'I don't think anybody will ever really know what makes Kerry tick. She's too complicated. Finds it hard to let go. Takes life so much more seriously than a girl like myself. I believe in taking life at its face value, making the best of things and not asking too much. Kerry's a perfectionist. She could never, for instance, accept love for an hour. For her it must be for life or it isn't love, and, well—anything that isn't just disgusts her.'

'My God,' said Steve. 'How well you know her.'

'She's a mixed-up kid—she fell good and proper for that super egotist husband of hers. I warned her she'd never make a go of it but she felt sure he loved her and off she went. She doesn't believe like I do in that Rupert Brooke poem—*"I dreamt I was in love with the One before the Last"*. It's always like that with Luke.

47

His wife—his girl friend—or a new model—they follow each other and there's always a One before the Last, then another after and another after that. Well, Kerry can't take it. Her own love is absolute and she demands absolute love in return.'

Steve took a long drink. The woman watching him could see that his hand was shaking. He was a good fellow, she thought with pity; so much more worth while than Luke. What a life! Nobody ever seemed to fall for the right person and the answer was always a lemon. That was why she recognized the fact that the lemon was bound to be at the bottom of the basket so one must set out to enjoy the luscious grapes before reaching rock-bottom. You could have a very good time if you didn't ask too much and lived only for the moment.

But, of course, thought Joanna, I'm a bit of a wanton in my way and I know it. That's something Kerry could never be.

Didn't she know how worried the girl had been about taking that week's holiday with Steve, even after all Luke's disgraceful infidelities.

Steve said:

'I've always wanted to give Kerry absolute love but she doesn't seem to want it from me. That's the rub. It's still Luke she wants.'

Joanna pushed the gin bottle towards him.

'Have another go and don't look so glum. I think it may work out for you in the end. I spoke to Kerry on the phone when she first got back and she said she'd had an absolutely heavenly time in Florence and felt heaps better and for all I know she may have undergone a mental transformation as well. She may be deciding to leave Luke and turn to you.'

Steve handed his cigarette case to Joanna, who shook her head.

'No, thanks, chum. I've a throat. Time I stopped puffing. I'm a ruddy chimney.'

Steve lit the cigarette for himself and examined the ash.

'What is your frank opinion of Kerry's husband?'

'I don't like him. I'm prejudiced. The man is incapable of being faithful, and from what Kerry tells me it happens often, and Luke is brutal and cold-blooded about it. I don't like cold-blooded men.'

Steve said:

'It makes my own blood run cold to think of Kerry living with such a man.'

'Yet he has a strange attraction. I can see why Kerry was so taken in,' said Joanna reflectively. 'That sort of satyr-fawn type, with his long black beatnik hair and his burning eyes and all his talk about beauty and philosophy and Michelangelo and the rest of the artistic jargon, it attracts a quiet innocent type like Kerry. It has its fascination for a lot of women, although never for me. I like good healthy love affairs and plenty of them. Luke's too much of a reptile. On the other hand, he can be pitied. He started with a chip on his shoulder. He came from nothing, you know. He educated himself, and like so many of his kind he's inwardly a snob. He liked the idea of marrying a lady like Kerry and she is a *lady* if there ever was one, although I don't like the word. A real aristocrat is our Kerry.'

'You're right,' said Steve under his breath. 'That part of her was what Luke first fell for as well as her beauty.'

'Do you see much of Luke?'

'No,' said Joanna. 'Between us it's a fight to the death. We loathe each other. He doesn't approve, he says, of my way of life and doesn't think Kerry ought to see much of me. Funny Ha-Ha, isn't it, when you think of *his* farm-yard morals!' chuckled Joanna, jangling her bracelets. 'I'm all that Kerry has left of her own relations and when I'm with her I'm just the loving cousin-cum-Momma who wants to look after the poor little girl. I don't do her harm.'

'I know. She's told me how good you are to her,' said Steve.

'I'm glad she's fond of me.'

'And can you tell me exactly how fond she is of *me?*'

'Deeply fond,' said Joanna, and the wistful boy's look in Steve's eyes touched her. She understood now why Kerry was so devoted to this lover of hers.

'Don't you know?' she went on.

'I suppose I do. She doesn't really love me, as I say. It's Luke. But it did seem while we were abroad, as if a miracle took place. We were so very happy. The weather was marvellous. We swam in a lovely pool in our villa's grounds and lay in the sun all day, ate wonderful meals, went over all those beautiful churches and picture galleries in Florence, sat out in the piazzas drinking coffee, danced in the evenings. I can't tell you how happy we were. We were so close . . .' His voice trailed away.

'And?' Joanna prompted.

'Then we came home!' Steve said flatly. 'And from the moment our plane touched down, Kerry seemed to change—become her old taut, restless, remote self. Our actual parting at the airport was hell. I wanted to take her back to the studio but she insisted upon going alone. It was as if she had finished with me—as if all our happiness and our loving companionship had been put behind her. It counted for nothing now we were back.'

'Maybe she just didn't want Luke to see her with you?'

'No, it wasn't that. She wanted to get away from me. It was just as if she was in a tearing hurry to get back to *him*, blast it. Yet, we all know life as she leads it with him is hell—it doesn't make sense.'

51

Joanna lifted her arched brows and she said with a sigh:

'Does love ever make sense?'

Steve's face reddened.

'Yes. There's nothing in the least complicated about my love for Kerry. It is and always will be. I want to marry her, have children with her, grow old with her. I suppose that sounds corny to you!'

Joanna smiled.

'No. It sounds fine. But you are a very uncomplicated person, Steve. We aren't all the same, honey. Probably few of us women ever are as simple and straightforward in our way of loving. Take me, for instance. No doubt it has crossed your mind to wonder how and why I live as I do and am, in a way, happy. I'll tell you. When I was seventeen I fell in love with a married man—a surgeon. For two years I was his mistress. I doted on him. Then one or two people found out and we realized that to continue this affair was to endanger his career. He was prepared to risk it, but I wasn't. There was no question of a divorce—he was a Roman Catholic and there were three children. So I left him. He was the only man I ever loved or wanted to be married to. Since then, there have been many men in my life but never, never have I been in love again. That's why I said earlier that love and happiness don't necessarily go together. I make love and like it. I laugh and men like me. But real happiness?

Boy, it doesn't exist except in books and dreams. Listen to cynic-Jo!'

Steve looked at her with a new sympathy and understanding.

'I'm sorry!' he said. 'Kerry never told me your story. But while it explains you—it doesn't explain *her.* She is young. She has her whole life in front of her—many years in which to build up a new life. It isn't as if she has any deep prejudice about divorce; and there are no religious bars to a divorce; she already has enough evidence on Luke to obtain six decrees. Why won't she leave him?'

'She still loves him! It's as simple as that. You've heard before now about women clinging on to the hand that beats them.'

'You loved your doctor, but you left him.'

'Yes, but because there was no hope and it was for his sake. I could only have brought him worry and perhaps dishonour. Perhaps Kerry feels that one day Luke will reform if she hangs on. She seems to care for him in a way none of his other girls have ever done. She may sense his real need for her, and he himself is probably unaware of it. But one day he may realize it. I'm just guessing, Steve, but it could be so.'

He nodded miserably.

'I suppose you are right. I've suspected something of the sort all along. If I thought it were possible for her to ever find real happiness with him, I'd try to bring myself to get out of her life. But can people change, Joanna? Do *you* believe he will reform and begin to appreciate her as I do?'

'No, I don't. I think he is too selfish and immoral. Truly immoral. He is also entirely physical in his affairs. I don't think he is ever capable of loving Kerry as you love her. But he could perhaps grow to need her in time, and that could be enough for Kerry. More even than love, she needs to be needed, and particularly by Luke.'

'But I need her!' Steve cried, then lowered his voice. 'I don't think Kerry has the slightest idea how much—or if she does, it doesn't touch her deep down inside. She wants me to care for her and spoil her but she doesn't want me to make any demands on her. She struggles all the time to stay un-involved. Yet during our week together, I felt she had given up the struggle, and decided not to fight any more. We were closer than we've ever been. We were happy, Joanna. I know it.'

'You haven't seen her since you came back?' Steve shook his head.

'I've phoned her three times—every other day to be precise. Each time she has some reason for not being able to meet me. Luke had 'flu and the doctor was coming round, or two days later, she had to go and collect some new oil paints for him as he wasn't well enough to go out himself. Or as yesterday when I rang, she was just too tired. She kept the

54

conversation on a strictly impersonal note and when I told her I loved her, all she replied was: "I know. Thank you." As though I'd just offered her a box of chocolates.'

Joanna was silent a moment. Then she said:

'Listen, Steve, I'll make a point of seeing her tomorrow. After we've talked, if you give me a number where I can ring you, I'll let you know how I find her. Luke doesn't like me calling at the studio but this once he can lump it. I'll just turn up there. I can produce a skin like a rhinoceros if I want. He can't *throw* me out!'

When Steve left Joanna Heyler's flat he felt a little better. Joanna had that effect—a warm comforting effect. But she didn't feel so sure of being able to help him. She knew her Kerry.

When Joanna called at the studio the following mid-morning, Luke was out.

'He's gone to see an artist friend in Kingston,' Kerry replied to Joanna's question.

She hugged her cousin warmly and added:

'I'm so glad you've come, darling Jo. I was feeling pretty depressed and then suddenly you appear like a fairy godmother to cheer me up. You look very smart as usual, Joanna. I like that black linen and white hat. I feel a mess.'

You look it! Joanna thought sadly, but was too kind to say it. She hated it when Kerry let herself go—too dog-tired to do her hair or face. There were great shadows beneath her eyes and under the sun-tan, she was hollow-cheeked. Her cotton shirt and slacks were paint stained, unpressed.

'I've been cleaning out Luke's studio!' she said apologetically.

'Couldn't he do that himself?' Joanna grumbled, taking off her hat and plumping herself down on the sofa.

'Oh, no, Joanna! You know Luke. He's frantically un-domesticated. He let everything go while I was away and since I came back, he has been quite ill, so nothing's been done. Sit down and make yourself comfortable. I'll make some coffee.'

While Kerry was in the kitchen attached to the studio, Joanna looked round with misgivings. There was nothing of Kerry's personality here. Luke's character dominated the flat. The studio was the only large room and was untidy and covered in dust. Kerry's efforts at cleaning certainly had made little impression on the general confusion. The skylight was filthy. The walls were hung with Luke's paintings. The floor was paint stained. There were great piles of books, papers and canvases. Such ornaments as there were were mostly pieces of modern sculpture which bore no resemblance to anything Joanna could recognize.

It was not the first time Joanna had been in the flat and she knew that Kerry was secretly ashamed of it.

'Really I'd like a more conventional home,'

she had confessed to Joanna. 'But Luke only wants this studio and our bedroom—he needs colour and effect to inspire him—and I think it would be wrong to make an artist live with something he didn't like.'

Joanna made a face. Kerry was too self-effacing. She should have exerted herself from the start—made Luke realize that marriage was a partnership in which two people and not just one had to be considered. Personally, Joanna could never have stood living in this studio for one day. Poor Kerry! She must long sometimes for a more restful, tasteful background to her life.

To be logical, she should have married Steve years ago. But then love was seldom logical.

Kerry came back with the coffee. The two cousins looked at each other.

Kerry thought:

How plump and jolly and well-balanced Joanna is. Why can't I be like her? My whole life is a muddle. It must be something in me that creates confusion wherever I go.

Joanna said:

'Tell me about your holiday with Steve. How was it, Kerry?'

The younger girl's fine-boned haunting face suddenly lit up.

'It was marvellous!' she said warmly. 'I had a wonderful time, Jo. We had such fun . . .'

'You were happy, then, with Steve?'

'Yes! I don't think any girl could help being happy with Steve. He is the perfect lover—attentive, kind, completely unselfish. He treated me as though I was a piece of Dresden china, and I'm afraid I fairly lapped it up!'

Joanna put a lump of sugar in her cup and looked at her cousin searchingly.

'Yet you weren't tempted to make it a permanent state of affairs?'

Kerry's face clouded and became withdrawn, uneasy.

'No! Don't ask me why, Jo. I just don't know myself what holds me to Luke. I'd hoped that week with Steve would make me realize how awful my life is with Luke, how much happier I would be away from him. I feel much more secure with Steve. That's what is so inexplicable. I still had to come back to Luke, where there is no security at all.'

Kerry's voice sounded so despairing that Joanna tried to lighten the moment. With a chuckle she said:

'Maybe you are a masochist and you like tormenting yourself.'

'Perhaps. I can't explain it, anyhow. I've thought about it so much. Perhaps I'm too weak to make the effort to break up my marriage . . . I don't know!'

Joanna looked at her sadly.

'You're still nuts about that bastard, aren't you?'

Kerry stood up, walked across to the

58

fireplace and straightened a crooked picture that hung above it.

'I love him and hate him at the same time. I want to be with him, yet I can't bear being with him. Over and over again he hurts me and I just come back like some stupid half-wit for more. I suppose if I described this last week to you, you would think it hell—yet the strange thing is, I've been happy, too. I'm only half alive when I'm away from him. Luke is different when he is ill—helpless and rather childlike. He's demanding and petulant—a rotten patient—but utterly dependent on me. It's me he wants—not some other girl, Jo.'

'I don't suppose any other girl would put up with Luke ill!' Joanna commented caustically. 'Far be it from me to advise a married woman to leave her husband but frankly, I don't see how you stand it, Kerry. With Steve waiting for you with open arms, there's no need for you to do so. It's a complete waste of your life—and poor Steve's. And what a nice guy *he is.*'

Kerry's eyes, tormented, sorrowful, turned to her cousin.

'I know it isn't fair to Steve. But what can I do, Jo? I've told him a hundred times I won't leave Luke. Is it my fault that he keeps waiting and hoping? I wouldn't blame him if he chucked me over and found another girl. Sometimes I wish he would—and end it all.'

'Perhaps if he did, it would bring you to your senses. Steve has always been too available.

Kerry, tell me something. Do you honestly believe Luke still loves you right deep down?'

Kerry shrugged.

'Maybe not. He couldn't love me and be so cruel. But it doesn't seem to make any difference. I still can't walk out on him.'

It was impossible, she thought, to try to explain it all to Joanna. She couldn't understand it herself.

Logic propelled her towards ending this marriage. It was an easy road to peace of mind and happiness—the road with Steve at the end of it. Yet a bitter, incomprehensible chain held her captive to the man she had married. It was not because of the sacredness of the marriage vows. There had seemed to Kerry to be nothing very sacred in a registry office wedding. That had been all that Luke would agree to. He had blankly refused to be married in a church. It would be hypocritical, he had said, seeing that he was an agnostic. No, it was something deep down inside her that still lived on—a nameless something one called love. It forced her to go on hoping that somehow something would change Luke and life would have purpose again.

She knew that the week with Steve should have altered her outlook and settled the problem. But she was no nearer resolving it despite the fact that the holiday had been so perfect—full of sweet companionship and harmony. Steve had been an adoring lover but he had not touched the innermost core of her heart. That tiny part of herself remained stubbornly beyond Steve's reach.

They had been very close; there were shared jokes and memories, and moments of passion that made her half believe her real happiness lay in Steve's keeping.

How then did she bid Steve good-bye at the airport, feeling that one half of her remained with him and the other compelling her to hurry, hurry quickly back to Luke.

Luke! Kerry's wide mouth tightened apprehensively. She remembered the ghastly welcome she had received. She had been afraid as the taxi drew near the flat that she would walk in and find another girl there with him. She wasn't afraid of confronting such a person—only of the look of intense irritation she would see on Luke's face when he saw *her,* his wife, the annoyance in his voice as he accused her of not letting him know what time she was arriving!

But there had been no woman. Luke was alone in the studio, pale and shivering. His first words to her were:

'Thank God you got back earlier than I expected. I'm ill.'

She had dropped her case and hurried to his side. She was grateful for his need of her. It drove all memories of Steve right out of her mind. By the time she had Luke tucked up in bed and rung the doctor, she felt as though she had never been away. It seemed right and proper to be back in the big, draughty, dirty studio off Gloucester Road—instead of that glorious villa near Florence. Right to be facing a pile of unwashed crockery in the sink and dirty linen in the washing machine. This was her home. This was her man.

Luke asked her no questions. He was concerned only with his own health. He complained that he hadn't felt well for the past few days; that the stuffy London heat had been getting him down; that he'd bathed in the Serpentine and supposed he'd caught a chill. He grumbled because he had been left to look after himself—swore at her—then put his hot feverish hand on hers and said accusingly: 'I feel rotten!'

And when her eyes filled with tears and she put her arms around him he was quite affectionate and clung to her like a small sick boy.

For three days she had nursed him; getting up at night to give him cool drinks and tablets or remake the rumpled bed. She lost all the healthy glow she had gained in Italy and grew dead tired. Yet she was happy, caring for him. Once she had found him staring at her with a puzzled expression in his handsome, restless eyes, under their long dark womanish lashes. He was pathetically pale and haggard and quite gentle.

'I suppose I don't really deserve this

attention from you, Katriona.'

It had been a golden moment, worth as much and more than many of Steve's protestations of undying love. Thinking about it as she lay awake in the dark that night, it didn't make sense. She knew that Luke was selfish, without morals or intellect. *Why* value a back-handed compliment from a man like that! Why *marry* a man like that? Why, why, *why?*

She asked herself for the millionth time whether her feeling for Luke was, like his, purely physical. Certainly it had begun that way. Mentally they had never recognized each other.

Kerry had tried hard to understand Luke's childhood when he told her about it but it was so completely divorced from her own quiet conventional upbringing that she could picture it only with confusion. She felt unable to understand him or his parents. At first, she had not doubted that here was a truly artistic man frustrated and crazy to express himself. She excused Luke's egocentric behaviour and complete lack of self-discipline on account of his upbringing for some time. Then she had begun to doubt that Luke was, in fact, a genius. He obviously had talent of a kind. He produced bright, sometimes interesting designs and colours that other people like himself recognized as good. Sometimes he even sold them.

During her holiday in Italy, standing before a great painting by Michelangelo, she had asked herself if there was any real artistry in Luke or if his upbringing had destroyed it before it had a chance to dominate his soul. Maybe if he had known true poverty, beauty might have flowered just as it often did from the hands of the old Masters. But Luke's had been the post-war generation of 'never had it so good'. His council-house home had been furnished not with rough wood boxes, made by a craftsman who, humble but good, still could produce the fine line and lovely design of a true artist. Luke's father and mother brought him up to appreciate mass-produced furniture that was meaningless and uninspired—curtains and carpets without a redeeming feature, poor in colour and design.

Luke had not had to struggle. He was given canvas and paint by his doting parents. They indulged their only child and gave him everything he wanted. They had felt themselves amply rewarded when he won an art scholarship. But those youthful flashes of talent were few and far between. His love of art was shallow and overshadowed by the coffee bars; the dance halls; the films. He read comics and cheap paper-backs. His friends were flashy and no good to him. Some, pseudo-artists like himself.

After a small exhibition, sponsored in fact by an American woman who fell for him and was willing to pay—he came into his own. He sold quite a number of the bright modern 'splashes' which looked good enough in bright modern flats. He even achieved some sort of name. The teenage artists trooped to Luke Austin's studio for advice. And if some of the best looking of them learned about physical love as well as painting—who cared?

Luke gave merry little parties. He was often to be seen striding down the King's Road, Chelsea, with a picture under his arm, black hair blowing in the wind, dark, bright eyes looking caressingly into the eyes of any pretty girl he passed, and wearing, generally, jeans and a black shirt with a colourful tie in the summer, or polo-necked black sweater, with corduroys, in winter.

He ran up bills in the art-material shops. He generally found some infatuated female to settle them. He always had an amusing anecdote for his men friends and made love lightly and gaily to the women. He was a popular figure and regular client in one or two of the Chelsea 'pubs'; standing outside with a group of other *soi-disant* artists, drinking, in the summer evenings; or going back to his studio on the colder nights, with a carrier-bag full of beer bottles. His girl friends of the moment supplied and cooked sausages and chips or an omelette.

Like Kerry, they stayed with him—hypnotized by those handsome burning eyes, that arrogant handsome face with the high-bridged nose and sensual mouth and the atmosphere Luke created of devil-may-care and know-all where there was no real knowledge.

He bluffed his way through discussions on the great Masters and the great paintings of the world. He was a glib talker. Most of his friends left his studio reviling him but returned, fascinated, unable to keep away. And he kept some of them by showing sudden flashes of generosity and sympathy.

Always robbing Peter to pay Paul, of course, borrowing from a man or woman with money, to help a genuinely starving painter or an old woman about to be flung out of her home because she hadn't paid the rent. Nobody quite knew how, when or where Luke would perform these sudden unexpected acts of compassion and charity. But he gained through them a really undeserved reputation for being a Good Samaritan. Running parallel with these episodes were the shameful acts; the cruel lack of feeling under the veneer of the passionate lover; the utter disregard for innocence or genuine affection. The brutal egotism.

This was the Luke whom Kerry first met—at a party in Battersea where a number of artists were gathered together and among them Luke. He was sitting in a corner, making lightning sketches of the guests; Luke, at that time, looking particularly sardonic and queerly attractive with a black pointed beard. (She had made him shave that off before they married and he had not grown it again.) The moment he saw her, he left the circle of women around his chair. He approached her, his eyes half shut and looked at her as though he were mentally undressing her from head to foot. It had been an outrageous look that angered her—yet captivated her. The man himself captivated her. Within five minutes she was sitting for him and he was asking her about herself, and telling her his personal story.

She told him that she had just finished a domestic course (she was nineteen then) and meant to go in for professional cooking. She adored it. She didn't want to be a secretary or model like all her friends. Rapidly outlining her lovely figure and face, Luke had said:

'You're out of your mind. You're so fantastically beautiful. Cooking! *Christ!* Pack it up. *"Come live with me and be my love!"* he quoted in his silkiest voice. 'If you must cook—cook for me in my studio.'

Within a week she was crazily in love and he was her lover.

So to him she became his 'Psyche', his idol and his love.

She was lost—utterly lost. She knew it but couldn't listen to Jo or any of her more sensible, far-seeing friends who mistrusted Luke. One of her admirers, Bill Stellent, a nice boy in the Civil Service, who had constantly proposed to her, told her he would regret all his life that he had taken her to that party where she had first met Luke.

And Steve above all others. Steve fought madly to stop her from going to Luke. Luke, the phoney, the schizophrenic, the breaker of hearts. Steve didn't want Kerry's heart to be broken. He knew her intrinsic worth. He adored her, not only her haunting beauty and grace but that touching domestic quality that made her so feminine and quaint and old-fashioned.

Once he dared to say:

'The fellow is worthless, Kerry, little better than a beatnik, a teddy-boy!'

She hadn't been offended. She had laughed. (Kerry had then been so radiant, so utterly happy, she believed in Luke, in herself, in deathless love; believed in Luke as an artist, a man, a lover.)

'Dear old Steve—how Victorian of you! Who cares what Luke is.'

'You don't know what you're doing, Kerry. You've led a more or less sheltered life with your aunt and father. You don't belong to Luke Austin's crowd. They haven't a moral between them.'

Her smoke-blue eyes danced at him.

'Nonsense. You don't know how marvellous Luke is under all that Chelsea art stuff. That's just a gimmick. Under it he is sincere—and one day you'll see he'll be famous.'

Steve went despairingly away.

The bottom dropped out of his world when Kerry abandoned all her shibboleths, all her faith in goodness and morality—and moved into the studio to live with Luke.

But for Kerry, for a time, all was perfect.

Life was fabulous and she lived it only for Luke. He took complete possession of her mind as well as her body. She was virtually hypnotized by him. He could do no wrong. She grew accustomed even to dirt and squalor and to standards which, before she met Luke, would have seemed impossibly low. She also hypnotized herself into believing that she was now in the right *milieu*. That it suited her to clean up the place after his bottle-parties; entertain for him; go out with him. She was proud of her position as his chosen love. 'Living in sin' meant nothing; it was a stupid outworn phrase. Real love condoned all. Life with Luke was exciting, enthralling, and soon she could live no other. To begin with, Luke was genuinely proud of this exceptional girl with her dignity, her cool uncommon beauty and her culture. The line of a famous poem . . . the name of a famous picture . . . she always knew them . . . he would ask her such things; stand in a crowd with his arm around her and smirk at his friends.

'Katriona knows . . . Katriona is a clever, clever girl. And Luke is clever—clever to have

69

found her . . . eh?'

A few words of praise like that were enough to compensate her for all the hard work she put in as Luke's girl friend. And the nights—the sweet, warm, feverish nights lying in his arms on the big divan in the little room opening out of the studio; feeling the wild hunger of his mouth—his long slim poetical body—giving him all that a woman had to give. They were the *raison d'être* for her very existence.

Until she began to speak of marriage—and children.

The first time she brought up the subject he scowled at her, then burst out laughing.

'Don't be funny, my precious.'

'It isn't funny. I mean it. I want to be your wife. I want your child.'

'God, darling—be your age! Grow up. I'm not a family minded man. You know that. We're very happy as we are. I've never been so happy, or for so long,' he added genuinely.

That warmed her heart but she looked at him anxiously.

'We weren't brought up quite in the same way. A lot of people I know think we ought to get married, darling Luke.'

'Tell 'em to drop dead, dearest.'

Kerry watched him painting in silence for a moment, fascinated as always by the graceful movements of his slender, stained fingers. Then she moved up to him and pushed the heavy dark hair back from his face which was pale and tense with concentration.

She knew suddenly that she wanted above all things to feel secure with Luke. She actually wondered for the first time if Luke's love for her was genuine if it did not include a wish to marry her. She began to argue and he spoke to her brutally.

'Oh, for God's sake, Katriona, shut up! I've told you how I feel. Don't, please, let this marriage idea become an obsession with you. Why can't you go on being happy as you are? You *are* happy living here with me, aren't you?'

She nodded and left him, in tears. But something had happened. Happiness wasn't possible any more.

One day, months later after a terrible scene, she left him, realizing that the rows were getting more frequent and that she must get away from him to think more objectively about Luke and her future—the whole set-up.

Perhaps if Luke had not bothered to follow and get in touch with her, the whole affair might have ended then. At that stage, she still had some will of her own left and some kind of pride that would not allow her to give in to him.

But Luke, strangely enough, refused to let her go. His male vanity had been sorely piqued. She was the first girl who had walked out on him and he still found her necessary to him. He refused to accept the end of an affair

71

of which *he* was not yet tired. Until now, he had never found a mistress more attractive to him. Cultured, intelligent, educated and—until she met him—sexually innocent.

She angered him at times but always intrigued him. Luke pursued her. But he found that he could not talk her into coming back to him without marriage. Again and again he stormed out of her presence, swearing never to see her again. But he loathed the studio without her and her refusal to live with him any longer stimulated his desire to conquer her. He could not bring himself to accept defeat at her hand.

Marriage, once he was finally brought to the point of having to consider it seriously, began to seem less unattractive and impossible. Divorce was always there—easy, even State-aided these days. Marriage need not last if either of them got bored with the other . . .

He gave in one day.

'Very well, we'll get married if it means all that much to you!'

She went back to the studio as his wife.

Marriage turned out to mean little more than ten minutes at a Registrar's Office, signing a paper, paying a fee and returning to the old way of life together. It didn't change Luke, although it did change Kerry in a queer way. She was now totally and whole-heartedly his; his wife, and she imagined, his last love. Luke had preferred her when she was more of an enigma; when he had to fight for her. She became too wholly his—too vulnerable—too sweet. He didn't want all that she showered him with. He didn't want to be emotionally tied to her just because she wore a wedding ring. He began to retreat within himself; irritated by Kerry's huge reproachful eyes if he swore at her or rejected her tenderness. He began to fill his life with other interests that she could not share. Finally, there were other women and Kerry was shoved into the background. Lonely, suspicious, heart-broken after his first infidelity she had been still too trusting to suspect what was going on at the studio.

Luke relaxed and became careless, then. When Kerry did discover the truth, she fought it—fought for her love, but surprisingly enough to him, made excuses for him.

'I realize that you have temptations other men probably don't have—that last girl modelling in the nude for you—obviously she tried to seduce you. But, Luke, we've only been married a *year!*'

She stopped, trembling with nerves and misery.

He didn't tell her it had been going on for the last nine months. He said:

'Well, if you don't like the way I am, you'd better divorce me. My pals warned me I'd never make a family man. I warned you. Remember?'

But Kerry had refused to accept her congé. She was fantastically stubborn in her way of loving.

'You're just trying to hurt me because I've made you feel guilty. Oh, Luke, can't you understand. I'm terribly upset, darling, and jealous—but I am trying to *understand.* Give me time and I shall probably get over it. You aren't in love with your model, are you?'

He'd been too surprised to prevaricate. 'Good God, no!' he said.

At once her eyes lit up—her smile returned.

So, she thought triumphantly, he still loves me. I shall never leave him. The other women are just playthings to him. He can't help it. *But I am his wife.*

CHAPTER FOUR

Joanna looked at her young cousin with concern. Kerry's thin expressive face was not only sad but tormented. Joanna said, gently:

'I don't think you are hard-boiled enough to go on living with a man like Luke. You need a chap like Steve to look after you, Kerry.'

Kerry's smile trembled at the corners of her mouth.

'I know!' she said. 'Sometimes I'm tempted to give up the fight and let Steve take charge. Once or twice in Italy I very nearly made up my mind to do it. Then, on the way home, I suddenly realized that I was anxious to get back to Luke. I can't think *why!*' she added with a confused laugh. 'I hate this studio flat. I wish we could move—live in the country. But Luke would hate that. Just as he hates the mere idea of me having a baby. Yet I wanted a child terribly—once.'

Joanna put down her empty coffee cup and was about to tell Kerry what she thought of Master Luke when the front door bell rang.

Kerry frowned.

'Don't know who that can be. I'm not expecting anyone.'

She disappeared. A moment later she came back with a girl, possibly about nineteen or even less. Summing her up quickly, Joanna guessed that the girl was an art student. Thin, pale, unkempt. She wore black fishnet stockings, flat shoes and an orange coloured, cotton sheath dress. Her hair was as black as her stockings and fell untidily around a chalk-white face—a sullen, defiant face.

'It's really Luke Austin I've come to see,' she said, staring from Kerry to Joanna with a backward tilt of her head. Her eyes were heavily made up, sloe-brown, almond shaped. She looked foreign to Kerry but spoke English with an accent that suggested the North Country rather than the Continent.

'Luke's out!' Kerry said firmly.

Some instinct warned her that this girl with

75

her wild hair and eyes was not going to be good for her.

'Then I'll wait!' the girl said. She had a sulky, slow voice. She began to drag off her red scarf.

'He may not be back until after lunch,' Kerry told her. 'Could I give him a message?'

The girl looked Kerry over with her quick nervous movement of the head and eyes. Then she asked bluntly:

'Are you the wife, then?'

Kerry's lips tightened. She nodded her head. 'And her?'

The girl indicated Joanna, who stood up with a jangle of bracelets and an extra tinge of pink on her plump cheeks.

'A relation!'

Kerry would have liked to add 'that is no business of yours!' but said nothing. Then she felt that unpleasant foreboding again. She said:

'Can I give my husband a message?'

The girl hesitated and then decided to sit down on the sofa. She took a crumpled packet of cigarettes out of her pocket and lit one. Looking up at Kerry she gave her a decidedly inquisitive stare and said:

'No, I'd best wait. I've been trying to see him for a week but he hasn't turned up. It's important.'

'He has been ill,' Kerry said. She looked at Joanna for help but her cousin remained silent and busied herself powdering her nose.

'I really don't think it is worth waiting. He *might* not be back till this evening. I just don't know,' Kerry went on awkwardly.

The inquisitive expression on the young stranger's face was suddenly replaced by one that could be called compassionate. A look that baffled Kerry. It was as if the girl were saying aloud: *'You, too!'*

'I must wait!' was her next remark. 'Like I've said, it's *important*. I can't leave it no longer.'

'Can we help?' Joanna asked, speaking for the first time.

The girl gave her a long, steady stare.

'I suppose you might, at that!' she said at last. Her gaze swung back to Kerry. 'You'll have to know sooner or later anyway, so I s'pose it might as well be sooner. If *he* doesn't tell you, I will, so what's the odds!'

She read the bewilderment on the face of Luke's beautiful wife and again, her own was momentarily softened by pity. Watching the two, Joanna began to sense the truth. It gave her a nasty jolt. Her plump face grew very serious indeed and she drew nearer Kerry as though ready to protect her.

Then the visitor looked first at one—then the other.

'I'm Gemma Phillips. I'm eighteen—and I'm pregnant! Now you know.'

Her voice was harsh, defiant, threatening.

Joanna heard Kerry gasp. She reached out a hand and put it on her cousin's shoulder. She answered the girl.

'Are you telling us you're having Luke's child?'

'Not if I can help it. But it's his all right. I warned him a month ago it was pretty much of a cert. Now it is—I am. I got it confirmed this morning. Three months, I am. I've got to get a move on if I'm going to get rid of it, too.'

'Oh, *no!*' The protest was wrung from Kerry. It was as though she could bear no more.

Gemma Phillips, cigarette between her lips, stared up at Luke's wife with that mixture of defiance—and pity.

'Sorry if it's a shock,' she went on. 'It was to me, too, I can tell you. He's told me all about *you.* Said you weren't in love with him any more but refused to divorce him. You aren't a bit like I thought—too good for him, I'd say.'

Kerry tried to speak but could not. She drew away from her cousin and sat down heavily. Her heart was pounding. She wanted to hate this girl—to scream ugly words at her—insult her. But through the wild confusion of her thoughts and emotions, she was aware that it was Luke who was at fault . . . Luke. Kerry covered her face with her hands.

She heard Joanna's voice, calm and quite in control of the situation as she asked:

'Look here, have you come to ask Luke for

money?'

'S'right! It'll cost a hundred or so I've been told. He'll have to fork out. I'm not having the kid. Not for no one.'

Joanna felt sick—for the girl and for Kerry. She made an effort to be dignified.

'You realize that what you intend doing is a crime, don't you?'

The girl shrugged.

'What else can I do?'

'You could have it. There are Homes where you could go. You could get the baby adopted.'

'No, thanks very much. I've my job to think of. I'm an artist's model. For the nude. The baby would ruin my figure, not to mention that I'd be out of the swim for months. You've got to be on hand in this game—s'easy to get overlooked if you vanish for any time. I'm just beginning to get known—get a few decent jobs with artists and at art schools. You might not think so but I've got a good figure.'

She unbuttoned her white coat and ran her hands over her small breasts and slim hips.

Joanna thought:

Oh, God, the poor pathetic kid!

Kerry tried to fight the desire to rush out of the studio and vomit. She broke out suddenly, rather harshly.

'It would be different, wouldn't it, if Luke could marry you. You'd want the child then. It's true that I've said I wouldn't divorce my husband, but this makes a difference. I'll let him go—if the child is his. I wouldn't want to have any part in—in . . .'

'Murder!' Joanna said, breaking in and looking hard at Gemma. 'That's what it would be, my dear.'

Gemma went on smoking. Kerry noticed suddenly the delicacy and beauty of her long thin hands and small ankles and her white skin.

Gemma said:

'As to marrying Luke, I'd rather have the child than do that! I'm not in love with him and he isn't with me. We both of us couldn't care less.'

'Then why . . . ?'

Gemma laughed.

'Aren't you old fashioned!' she jeered at Kerry. 'Not Luke's type at all, you aren't. I'll tell you about it. Me and Luke met at a coffee bar—went on to a pub and made a night of it. Next day I sat for him *and* I slept with him. He's attractive, okay, but marry him—no thanks. I'm not marrying him or no one not for years. I don't want to be saddled with kids and all that washing and cooking. I had enough of that at home. Eight of us there was, and me the eldest so I had to do Mum's job for her most of the time. Up in Leeds, it was. No, thank you. No marriage or kids for Gemma Phillips. As a model I earn enough to keep myself, with two girl friends sharing a flat in Earl's Court. We have a good time.'

'You realize that if you go ahead with your plans, I could report you to the police?' Joanna said suddenly and firmly.

Gemma stared back at her unconcerned. 'Who are you anyhow?'

'Mrs. Austin's cousin.'

Gemma laughed.

'Ever so helpful you are. Well, listen to me. If you report me, I'll involve *her*—'

She nodded at Kerry. 'Papers 'ud get hold of it and there'd be a bit more nasty muck-raking. The press would like it, me being an artist's model and all.'

She stretched long, slim and quite graceful legs.

'Don't—please don't!' Kerry broke out. She wasn't sure if she could stand much more of this. Joanna again took charge. She stood up and looked down at the visitor.

'Look—you'd better clear off. Mrs. Austin and I will think about what is best to do. But don't run away with the idea that Mr. Austin has any money. I might be able to help you but it wants consideration. It won't hurt you to wait another twenty-four hours. Give me your address and I'll get in touch with you, but just leave my cousin alone!'

For the first time, the girl looked uneasy, even ashamed. Her pale face flushed. Her lips quivered.

'I'd rather wait for Luke . . .' she began, but Joanna took her firmly by the arm and led her towards the door. 'You're not waiting here. This is my cousin's home. And I'm sure you know the kind of man Austin is. He won't be all that sympathetic with you. No, he'll be mad that you've come here and told his wife the facts and he'll probably try to deny the parenthood. Maybe it won't be easy for you to prove he's the father. Take my word for it—you'll do better to leave this in *my* hands. I'm likely to be a lot more generous than Luke.'

The girl looked from Kerry to the plump, blue-eyed older woman. For a moment she hesitated. She did not seem so sure of herself. She stubbed her cigarette end on an ashtray with an angry, jabbing movement.

'Okay—twenty-four hours. Here's my card. I had some printed for my job,' she added almost proudly.

Kerry's gaze—blurred, shocked, wretched, barely saw the name on the cardboard.

Miss Gemma Phillips,
11 Madison Mansions,
Earl's Court

When she had gone, taking with her a strong odour of cheap perfume, Joanna went back into the studio and put her arms round Kerry's shoulders. The girl was slumped on the sofa.

'This about winds up what I've been trying to tell you—you've got to leave him, darling.

Really! He's no good. This is the end, surely.'

Kerry lifted a wet, tortured face.

'It ought to be Jo, God knows. It's so sordid—so horrible. It doesn't seem real to me. I can't believe it. It's like one of those awful kitchen-sink dramas. The pregnant mistress coming to see the betrayed wife. You don't think that she made it up? That she's just trying to get money out of Luke?'

'No, I don't. She'd never have told us the facts if she'd been just out to blackmail Luke. Besides, there was some kind of ghastly integrity about the wretched girl. The sooner you get out of here the better. Pack a case and come home with me, honey.'

Kerry looked up at Joanna's kindly, friendly face, then round the studio in a desperate way. She knew that Joanna was right. This must be the end . . . her marriage was over finally. She ought not to be surprised by what had just happened; Luke had always been wickedly selfish and irresponsible. Joanna was right—he wouldn't even try to help the girl he got into trouble—he'd worm out of it if he could.

'What about the baby?' she asked Joanna suddenly in a hoarse voice. 'It's Luke's child.'

'It's better not to think about that,' Joanna answered hastily.

She understood Kerry's feelings about the child. She, too, was dead against the idea of abortion.

Kerry sat silent, doubled up, crushed by her

personal anguish and the creeping paralysis of her disillusionment in Luke.

Joanna tapped her cousin on the shoulder. 'Honey—look at me—listen.'

Kerry stared up at her, her eyes confused. 'Well?'

'If you're worrying about the girl, and Luke won't help her, I will.'

Kerry's face flushed a dull red.

'It's not your responsibility, Jo. Besides, I'm not sure we ought to make it easy for her to get rid of the child.'

'You surprise me. I thought you pitied her.'

'It isn't that I lack pity for her. But it is wrong. We would be condoning a wrong, aiding and abetting. And besides, it's Luke's child.'

'Oh, dear God!' exclaimed Joanna, her round pretty face thoroughly disgusted. 'You can't, after all this, *care* about Luke or his offspring. If you do, you're mad. You're destroying yourself, Kerry.'

Kerry's eyes clouded.

'It's sweet of you to offer to help, Jo, but please let's wait and face Luke with it. I might make him accept his responsibilities for once in his life.'

'For God's sake, Kerry—you're living in a dream world. Luke will never be any different.'

'All the same, I *must* try. Luke's an artist, Joanna. You just can't judge him by ordinary standards.'

Joanna groaned, shook her head despairingly and lit a cigarette.

'I give up. You can't want to stay with this man—not now.'

Kerry got up and began to walk up and down the studio. She felt hot, feverish, incapable of clear thought or action.

'I know you think I'm crazy, Jo,' she said huskily, turning to face her cousin, 'but I must act as I think best.'

Joanna said no more. She opened her bag, drew out a key and handed it over to Kerry.

'Here you are, lunatic. The flat key. If things become unbearable—pack up and join me, any day, any time. I'll always be pleased to have you.'

Kerry burst into tears. Joanna left her like that—unable to help or advise any more, and near to tears herself.

Kerry was not conscious of time. She went into the kitchenette and began to prepare a meal, lost in the unhappiness of thought, still suffering from the shock that Gemma Phillips had given her.

Luke came home at six o'clock. He was in a good mood. He banged the front door behind him and came into the studio with a bundle of canvases stacked under either arm. His narrow dark eyes smiled at Kerry.

'Guess what!' he greeted her amiably. 'Derek sold two of my paintings and got thirty-five and forty-five quid for them.'

He dumped the canvases onto the sofa and stood, hands on narrow hips, staring down at his wife.

'Well, aren't you going to congratulate me?'

Kerry's heart turned over. The sick feeling returned. Bitterness choked her. Had it not been for Gemma, this would indeed have been an occasion for congratulations and celebration. Luke was in an excellent mood, anxious for her approval. How she had longed for such moments. And Luke, when he smiled at her in that slightly oriental, close-lidded way, was unbearably attractive. She said quickly:

'Gemma Phillips has been here!'

Luke's face froze. His whole expression changed.

'Oh? We're not in for one of your scenes, I hope!'

She ignored that.

'Luke, she came to ask you for money. She's pregnant.'

Now, for a single instant, she saw shock register on Luke's face. Then it became withdrawn, evasive.

He said:

'So what? That's her worry!'

'Oh, Luke!' It was impossible, after all, to keep the horror from her voice. 'Luke, it's *your* child.'

Luke laughed.

'How the hell do you know? Why, that girl

sleeps around with a dozen or more types. Damned if I'm going to be blamed for it.'

It had never occurred to Kerry that Luke would take this attitude. She was shaken. She said:

'I do believe her. You must marry this girl so she can have the baby.'

Again for one split fraction of time, shock registered on his face. Then he stared at her brazenly and said:

'So the ever-faithful is giving up the ghost, eh? I wondered how much longer it would be before you packed it up, Katriona!'

She swallowed, the sound of her name on his lips still holding the power to hurt her when she least expected it.

'You always thought you were too bloody good for me, didn't you? Now I suppose you're chortling because I've proved you right—or at least you think I have. Just like you to take that little tramp's word against mine. Never would give me the benefit, would you?'

'Oh, Luke, that's not true. But you can't deny this. You don't deny it, do you?'

She wasn't aware that she had given herself away. He knew now that he could keep her if he wished. She wanted him to deny it; wanted him to be able to deny it. As always, he took delight in hurting her. It gave him the deepest pleasure of all to be able to humble her. It made him at least someone important because in his heart he knew she was worth a hundred of him.

'I'm not bloody well going to try to deny anything to you!' he jeered. 'If you've made up your mind to call me a black sheep, then I'll just have to be one.'

'Luke!'

He avoided the direct blue eyes. Sometimes he hated her enough to want to hit her. That innocent, hurt look drove him mad. She had the most infuriating way of making him feel inferior and only by humiliating her could he re-establish his superiority. He couldn't do it in bed—she was always ready to surrender. There was no longer any satisfaction in taking her body. He could only win by wounding her spirit.

'Well?'

'Luke, I've got to know the truth. Can't you understand that I have to know. If it's true this baby is yours, it's the end of our marriage. You've got to marry this girl. Otherwise she'll get rid of the baby.'

'I thought you already told me it was true. So what are you waiting for? Not that it will make any difference. It's not my fault the girl was stupid enough to get pregnant. A girl like that should know better.'

'Luke, you are equally responsible. Don't lie about it.'

'So now I'm to have to stand here and listen to a lecture on morals from my wife. Honestly, Katriona, I don't know why you don't just push off and have done with it. If you've made up your mind I'm no good, then what the hell is the point of you staying here?'

She guessed he was bluffing. He was evading a direct answer to her question. He was guilty—if only he would admit to it the way he had admitted to those affairs with other women. Why not admit it? He didn't love her, Kerry, any more. He didn't care if she went. So why not admit the truth—if it was the truth. Was it? The doubt was there, planted in her mind as he had meant it to be. It took root, feeding on her desire for disbelief.

'Hell, I'm hungry. I missed lunch—we drank our lunch in the Crown. Anything in the kitchen, my love?'

It didn't mean anything—it was only Luke's affected way of speech when he was trying to be casual. Nevertheless, it touched that still open wound in her heart. My love, my love! Once she had been Luke's love. Once . . .

'Luke!' She was almost shouting now from nervous exasperation. 'You can't end the discussion like this. Gemma Phillips says the child is yours. She wants money to get rid of it. You've *got* to tell me the truth.'

Luke paused in the doorway, looking back at her with an expression which might almost have been of amusement. He said slowly:

'Here's one thing I'll tell you, Katriona. Nothing on this earth would make me marry Gemma Phillips. So go ahead and divorce me if you wish, but don't think by doing so I'm going to father a child I'm bloody sure isn't mine. And now shut up about it. If you're going, then for heaven's sake hurry up about it. If you're staying, then I want something to eat.'

He walked out, leaving her alone in stunned silence.

She tried to remember Gemma's face, as if from the impression she could be sure again that the girl was speaking the truth. But she was no longer sure. Luke's words had been strangely convincing—or was that just because she wanted so very much to be convinced. She had no reason to trust Luke—the opposite was the case. He could so very easily be guilty. On the other hand, Luke had never lied about his affairs. He'd been hurtfully and hatefully honest about them. Since he had never been much concerned with her opinion of him, he had not troubled to deny his liaisons. Why, then, should he bother now?

I'll never be sure! she thought hopelessly. If I leave him, it isn't going to help the girl—not if Luke refuses to acknowledge his paternity. She'll still get rid of it. The only hope for the baby is if he married her.

Suddenly Gemma's words came into her mind.

'As to marrying Luke, I would rather have the child than do that . . .'

Am I out of my mind? Kerry wondered.

Trying to marry my husband to a girl he doesn't love and who dislikes him, for the sake of a child which means nothing at all to *me* . . .

She sat down, her head in her hands. Never had she been less sure what she should do. Instinct told her to go, reason and Joanna backed up her instinct. But her desire was to stay and there was no logical explanation for that desire.

He's still my husband, she thought, as if the words could bring back the rightness of moral responsibilities.

She heard Luke singing in the kitchen and was amazed. He could not be guilty and sing so light-heartedly at the same time. Luke was accustomed to people like Gemma Phillips, understood their morals, their way of life. He might have slept with her but he was far too level-headed—and selfish—to permit any careless mistakes which might later rebound on him.

Kerry felt suddenly guilty. She and Joanna had been too ready to believe the worst in him—too ready to condemn. Jo never had liked Luke and made no secret of the fact that she wanted Kerry to leave him and marry Steve. Naturally she was prejudiced.

I, too, have been unfaithful! Kerry thought unhappily. So what right have I to condemn Luke. It's no excuse to say he provoked me into it. I have free will—I could have refused to go with Steve. The only decision I have to make is whether my leaving Luke will save the life of a baby that isn't wanted by father or mother. And Luke has answered that.

Slowly, as if movement were a painful effort, she rose to her feet and went to join Luke in the kitchen.

CHAPTER FIVE

Luke was changed—different in the way Kerry had longed and prayed for. It was as if the Gemma affair had wiped the slate clean, cleared the air, and made it possible for her marriage to Luke to be reborn in new fresh ground. The seedling of happiness which was emerging for Kerry was not yet a strong young plant. It was not yet flowering. But it seemed to her as if the roots were down safely in their new soil and with time and care, might flourish.

She was almost happy.

Luke's character had not changed. He was still sardonic, curt, selfish. But he was once more her lover.

The day that Gemma Phillips had come to the flat, she had been unable to trust Luke's sudden renewed desire for her. There were too many doubts still lingering in her mind. For the first time in her married life, she had refused to allow him to touch her. For a week she had withstood his demands—they were never pleas—as well as the demands of her own body which refused to be subdued by her mind. No matter what Luke did, her body weakly accepted the attractions of Luke's. She realized its nature was purely physical and fought with herself. And for a week she succeeded. But Luke, the ardent determined lover, was strangely irresistible. Mistrust him though she did, his kisses still stirred her to a helpless longing to surrender. The touch of his hands on her body repelled and fascinated her. He was never gentle—always demanding in an utterly masculine way that brooked no refusal. He did not use the words of a lover nor try to woo her with gifts, flowers, kindness. His daytime behaviour did not vary from the usual except that he was never far away from her. Cooking over the stove, she would feel him standing silently in the doorway, watching her from those dark, unblinking eyes. She would fight against the desire to look up at him just as she fought to remove herself from the proximity of his body when he sat down beside her, his thigh touching hers.

It was a strange, compelling, persistent demand for physical subjugation and the effort to withstand the silent assault left Kerry even more exhausted at the end of a week than she had been at the beginning. Finally, she surrendered and that night was like their first night together. There was no sweetness, no tenderness as there had been with Steve; perhaps not even any love; only a wild, pulsating, burning passion that consumed them both as the night gave way to dawn. And in the morning, it began all over again.

Kerry could not know, as Joanna suspected, that it was her very refusal of Luke that had reawakened his interest in his wife. He had been prepared for Kerry to walk out on him and would not have raised a finger to stop her. But the fact that he had so nearly lost possession of her had had a strange reaction. Suddenly, he desired her again. Her rejection of him had further fired his passion until it became more an obsession. He had to have her and he knew that he was the stronger of the two. He would, just as he had always done in the past with any woman he desired, succeed in the end. He waited his time—and was rewarded.

He did not tell Kerry that he had seen Gemma Phillips—nor that he had given her fifty pounds. He did not tell her that the girl had argued fiercely that she needed more or that he had refused to give it.

'You'll have to prove a paternity case against me,' he had said to her flatly. 'I'm not acknowledging responsibility. This money is just to help you out of a bad spot. And don't think you can blackmail me into giving you any more.'

To Kerry's question as to what had

happened to Gemma, Luke said airily:

'Forget her. It was just a try-on. We shan't hear any more from her.'

But Kerry could not forget the younger girl's plight. She worried about her on the few occasions when her mind was not taken up by Luke. Eventually, she went to Joanna and said:

'Will you send her this, Jo? Don't say whom it's from. I don't want any thanks.'

Jo looked at the five five-pound notes and gasped.

'Are you out of your mind, Kerry? That's a hell of a lot of money to give away. It's not Luke's contribution by any chance?'

Kerry shook her head.

'No, Luke doesn't even know about it. You can't expect him to pay for something that isn't his responsibility.'

Jo's eyebrows went up.

'Then why are *you* giving the girl money?' Kerry shrugged.

'Call it conscience money, if you like. I can't get her off my mind. It must be so dreadful to be in her position—having a baby and no money behind you.'

'I thought she was intending to get rid of it.'

Kerry looked at her cousin unhappily.

'Perhaps that is what I'm trying to avoid. If she has a little money, she might decide to have the baby after all. I thought that you might write to her—tell her that I'll send some more if she decides to keep the baby—at least until it can be adopted or something.'

Jo gave a deep sigh.

'My dear child, you are just "not with it". That girl hadn't the slightest intention of doing what was right. All she was concerned with was herself.'

'You don't know that!' Kerry argued. 'It could have been just a pretence. I don't think she was all hard. You have such a cynical view of human nature, Jo. I believe there is good in everyone if you look deep enough for it.'

Joanna shrugged and added sarcastically:

'I suppose that goes for Luke, too! I've yet to see the good in him.'

Kerry flushed.

'Please, Jo, don't be like that about Luke. He has changed—really he has. Luke doesn't find it easy to be gentle or sweet, but underneath he does love me. I'm more sure of it every day. Our marriage is going to work, after all, you'll see.'

For a moment Joanna was silent. Kerry sounded so young and trusting and full of hope. She just hadn't the heart to force her own opinion of Luke down the girl's throat. She believed without any doubts that Luke was responsible for Gemma Phillips' baby; the girl had been honest enough in her brief statement of facts—Jo was sure of it. Somehow, Luke had succeeded in making Kerry believe he was innocent and had once more evaded all his responsibility. Now the man had Kerry under his thumb again and poor Steve might as well not exist.

'*Will* you send the money for me, Jo?'

'Yes, yes, I'll send it. I think it's mad, wrong, and at the very best, quite unnecessary. However, if it's going to make you happier, I'll send it. Now let's have a drink. I could do with it.'

Kerry felt happier when she left Joanna's flat. The money had constituted most of her savings but somehow she knew it was better spent this way than on a new winter outfit. Now at least the poor girl had something behind her. It wasn't as if she, Kerry, were alone and in need. She had Luke . . .

She hurried her footsteps, knowing that Luke would be at the studio waiting for her.

'Must you go to Jo now?' he had said irritably. 'I want you here, Kerry. I feel like making love.'

'Oh, darling!' She had kissed him and almost given way to the touch of his hands. But then she had smiled and kissed him again and said:

'I won't be long, Luke. I promise. I'll come straight back.'

As she neared the studio, she felt a moment's sudden fear. Suppose Luke had got tired of waiting for her; had decided to go out . . . a few weeks ago she would not have dreamed of finding *him* waiting for *her* . . . But he was there, lying on the divan idly sketching on a pad across his knees. She went over to him and kissed the dark, untidy head.

'Luke, I do love you so much!' she whispered.

He pulled her roughly down on top of him.

'I know!' he said harshly. 'And I want you, too—like hell.'

It didn't occur to him to ask why she had wanted to see Jo; what they had talked about. Luke was never interested in her activities. But at this moment, the knowledge could not hurt her for she knew that Luke was interested only in her. And that was enough for now.

*   *   *

Joanna looked at the man who had come into the room with a sense of shock. Steve Manders had changed. He looked much older than his thirty-four years. Then she realized why; he was going grey.

'You look just the same!' he said, allowing her to take his coat and accepting the drink she held out to him. He was suddenly very pleased to see her. For a few hours, after her phone call, he was wondering whether it was sensible to accept her invitation to drinks in her flat. She had told him frankly that she wished to discuss Kerry with him. But it was more than half a year since he had seen Kerry—six months in which he had practically killed himself with work in order to erase her from his mind. Seeing her cousin, Joanna, was going to re-open a wound that had never properly healed.

But he had accepted and there he was, glad to be sitting in Joanna's comfortable flat, warmed by the electric fire, somehow comforted by her plump, friendly person.

'Nothing has changed in my life!' Jo said. 'Except that I've had another birthday and am, it is to be hoped, older and wiser! You look tired, Steve. Been over-working?'

'Probably!' Steve nodded. 'I also had a pretty nasty go of 'flu. I'm going grey, see?' He touched the silver at each temple and grimaced. 'Premature old age!' he said.

'Still the confirmed bachelor?'

Steve's eyes went swiftly down to his drink. Jo thought:

So he's still in love with Kerry. In a way, I'm sorry; in a way glad.

The silence was not awkward or unfriendly. After a moment, Steve looked up and said bluntly:

'I'll never marry anyone but Kerry. And now that is all over, I'll probably end my days a bachelor. Tell me, how is she? Well? Happy?'

'She's not ill!' Joanna said slowly. 'Nor is she well. She is living on a razor's edge and that plays havoc with her nervous system. As to being happy—no! I think she is resigned.'

Steve put down his drink and leant forward, his elbows on his knees as he searched

Joanna's face for an explanation. He felt his heart bumping uncomfortably in his chest.

'I thought everything was well with her. That . . . that she—and her husband were completely reconciled. She wrote to me, you know, after Italy, told me she was still in love with Luke; that they were making a fresh start and under the circumstances, she wouldn't be wanting to see me again.'

Joanna nodded, her eyes pitying. The very casualness of the man's voice told her too clearly how devastating a blow Kerry's letter must have been to him.

'I know. She told me she didn't think it fair to keep you hanging on hoping for something more than she could give.'

The understanding, maternal expression of Joanna's plump face stirred Steve to confide. For so long now, he had bottled up inside himself all thoughts of Kerry, of the past, the future he had once dared to hope for with her.

'I just don't understand why the break had to be so final. We could have stayed friends!' His voice was suddenly bitter. 'Did she imagine I only wanted to see her if she would go to bed with me? Great Scott, that was the least important part of our relationship. Her letter was like a slap in the face, Joanna. It was as if she was deliberately belittling my love for her; relegating it to mere lust!'

Joanna put a hand over his and said gently:

'I wish I'd seen you before now, Steve. I

100

could have explained that. You have to remember that Luke is Kerry's yardstick. For him, love is lust, passion, physical desire. It's the nearest he can get to giving anything to any other human being. The only way he has of expressing affection, if you can call it that. Therefore Kerry was bound to believe that physical expression was important to you, too. She told me she had written to you and why. She wanted desperately to keep you as a friend but felt it unfair to ask you to accept this lesser relationship. In a way, she was right, Steve. It wouldn't have been easy to go back to a platonic friendship after you had been lovers.'

'Not easy—but I would have done it. It's been hell, Joanna; not knowing what was happening to her; how she was; even where she was. Do they still live in that horrible studio?'

Joanna nodded. She got up and refilled their glasses, then pushed a packet of cigarettes across to the man.

'Yes! They still live there—if you can call it living. I call it an existence. I suppose it's hardly necessary to tell you that Luke's sudden passion for his wife died a speedy death. He was unfaithful to her again.'

'Oh, no!' Steve's voice was rough with pain.

'Yes! And as usual, Kerry forgave him. She told me about it and made all the usual excuses for him. Luke mustn't be measured by the same yardstick. He had temptations other men didn't have. It was the girl's fault. Luke was sorry . . . he hadn't said so, of course, but she knew he was. We mustn't expect him to change overnight—it would take time for Luke to settle down. And so on and so on.'

'My poor Kerry! *Why doesn't she leave him, Joanna?* That's what I simply cannot understand. He can't make her happy. He never has and he never will.'

Joanna sighed.

'Your remark is perfectly logical, Steve, but unfortunately women in love seldom are logical. And she loves him—the way women do love men like Luke. You hear of it time and again—women who are knocked about, cheated, used, abused . . . yet they go on loving. I've long since given up asking myself why. I accept that she loves him.'

Steve nodded.

'I've learned to accept it, too. But I'll never, never understand how Kerry—a girl like that . . . can live with such a man, far less love him.'

No, it did not make sense but being a woman, Joanna could at least understand how a girl like Kerry could stay constant despite every disaster. She might be physically frail but her capacity to love was strong enough to withstand setbacks. While she continued to have faith in Luke, she would bear everything for what she believed would be hers in the end. The question was, how long would that faith endure? How many more blows must she receive before belief in the myth that was Luke, the husband, was finally shattered?

'Look, Steve, you must be wondering why I asked you to come here. I'll explain.'

As quickly as she could, she told him about Gemma Phillips, her visit to the studio, Kerry's gift of money to her. Then she handed Steve a letter.

'This came in yesterday. I've been awake all night wondering what I ought to do about it. The fact is, for the first time in my life, I'm flummoxed. I just don't know what to do.'

Steve's eyes scanned quickly over the large, childish unformed handwriting that covered the cheap, scented note paper.

I'm writing to you because you are the only person that has ever been really kind for no reason. I don't suppose you've forgotten the money you sent me from Luke's wife, asking me not to get rid of the baby.

It's because you were both kind when you needn't have been that I'm writing now. I did mean to get rid of the baby—I tried but it didn't work. At the time, I thought I was the unluckiest girl in the world. Trouble was, you see, that I left it too late. Well, now I don't think like that. You see, I had the baby and he's turned out to be the only person in the world who matters a row of pins to me. I don't even care that he looks like his father—Luke Austin was never any good but I reckon that's because he's like me—he never got taught the right things when he was growing up. Well, I love my baby and I want what's best for him and they've told me here in the Home that he'll be best off adopted, seeing as how I haven't any money nor parents that'll look after him proper. That's why I'm writing to you. You see, I do know a bit about the world and I could tell Luke's wife was decent, like you—a different type from me. I wondered if maybe you could talk her into having my baby. After all, he is Luke's kid as well as mine. And she could bring him up proper. I don't want him to go to strangers and if she'd take him, I wouldn't worry about him so much.

I would have written to her myself but it was you that sent the money so I thought maybe you'd want to be the one to suggest it to her you know, that you might put it over better than me.

Yours faithfully,
Gemma Phillips'

Steve laid down the letter, speechless. He looked up at Joanna and frowned.

'I don't see what the problem is. Of course, what the girl wants is out of the question.'

Joanna nodded.

'That was *my* first reaction. I even got as far as writing to the girl to say so. Then I thought again and, Steve, I began to wonder if I was doing the right thing. After all, it isn't for *me* to decide for Kerry—for Luke—or for that wretched child. It has to be Kerry's decision. Hers and Luke's.'

'Surely you don't think Luke Austin would have it?'

'No, I don't! But Kerry might. She just *might*. That's the whole trouble, Steve. She's so soft-hearted she might take it. And especially if it does look like Luke. Then she's caught— she'll be responsible for it and if that marriage does bust up . . .'

Steve stood up, unable to sit still with his thoughts.

'I don't see how any woman could bring herself to take her husband's illegitimate child and bring it up as her own. Surely she would hate it—hate to be reminded of what her husband had done?'

'Probably most women would refuse. But I'm not so sure about Kerry. I'm just not sure, Steve. I know that to do so would be a mistake but I can't trust Kerry not to make that mistake, if Luke allowed her to. That I do doubt. But the question is, must I tell her? What do *you* think? If it were your decision, would you show her the girl's letter?'

Steve drained his glass and stubbed out his cigarette.

'Yes, I would. I'd let her know once and for all what kind of a man she had married. She's never been willing to look at Luke Austin and see what he is. This will show her. I don't think there's any danger she'll take the child. I don't see how she *could*.'

Joanna said softly:

'Suppose I were to offer you Kerry's child—a little girl that looked just like her in miniature. How would you feel then, Steve?'

'I don't know anything about babies. I'm not married. It couldn't happen.'

'That's prevaricating. Supposing it did?'

'But that is different!' Steve burst out. 'Don't you see that Kerry is utterly lovable. She's good, sweet, kind, innocent—all the things Luke Austin isn't.'

'What you are saying is that you love her. And she loves Luke.'

'I still think she'll refuse to take his child. My instinct is not to give her the choice, but I agree that morally you have to do so. It isn't your affair. She has to see that letter.'

Joanna sighed.

'I was afraid you'd say that. I only wish I had your conviction that she won't be tempted to take the baby. She has wanted a child—Luke's child, for a long while. It is Luke who refuses to have a family. This has come at a bad time, Steve, and I'm worried.'

'Then come out to dinner with me and stop worrying,' Steve said unexpectedly. 'Please do, Joanna, I'd be glad of your company.'

'I'd love to,' Joanna answered. 'I hope this

means I'm forgiven for dragging you in to this. I suppose it was cowardice on my part. I didn't want to make the wrong decision alone. Now I can feel we are sharing it. At the same time, that makes me feel bad as I've no justification for involving you.'

Steve's eyes were suddenly filled with an unbearable pain.

'Don't you think I'm already involved? I haven't been able to stop loving her, wanting her, thinking about her. I've plunged into my work like a beaver but still that doesn't stop me thinking about her at night when I'm trying to sleep. It's been hell, Joanna. Several times I have been sorely tempted to get in touch with you—just to get news of her. Each time I told myself that this was madness—the best way to get Kerry out of my system was to put the past right behind me. But it wouldn't stay there. I can't tell you what it means to me just to be able to speak Kerry's name aloud to someone else—to be able to say openly and honestly "I love her".'

Joanna went to him and put her arms round him and hugged him in a simple unconscious gesture of pity.

'I'm so sorry, Steve. Maybe one day . . .'

'Yes,' he broke in huskily. 'Where there's life there's hope, so people say. I shall never stop hoping.'

Joanna forbore to tell him that if indeed she did pass on Gemma Phillips's letter to Kerry,

Steve's hopes were in danger of being dashed for good. There was always the possibility that this would evoke a real point of discord between Kerry and Luke and Kerry end up leaving him, or Luke walking out on her.

They were on the point of leaving the flat—Joanna had her hand on the door when suddenly the bell shrilled, making them both jump.

Joanna frowned.

'Who on earth can that be? It's nearly seven o'clock. I'm not expecting anyone . . .'

She opened the door and stared at the figure confronting her.

'Kerry? What a surprise . . . come in . . . Steve's here . . .'

She broke off, seeing the somnolent expression on Kerry's face.

'Is something wrong? Come in, Kerry.'

Kerry walked into the flat and glanced up at Steve. With an obvious effort, she said hullo and then sank into one of the armchairs.

Steve had not moved. He was aghast at the change in her. He might have aged in the last six months, but Kerry had changed almost out of recognition. She was chalk-white, her face so thin and drawn that the bones stood out starkly beneath the tightly stretched skin. Her eyes seemed enormous. She looked ill.

A new emotion that was part pity, part anxiety and part love, swept over him so that he stepped towards her and then paused.

What could he do or say? Kerry had put him out of her life. It was not his place now to comfort her, show her his own concern for her.

Joanna glanced from her cousin to Steve and said quickly:

'Steve and I were just going out to dinner. Have you eaten, Kerry. Are you staying long?'

Kerry looked at her helplessly.

'My suitcase is downstairs. I wondered . . . I wanted . . . could I stay for a few days, Jo?'

'But of course!' Joanna said instantly, again glancing swiftly at Steve. He said then:

'We can skip the dinner. I expect you two girls will have things to talk about so I'll push off.'

'Oh, no, don't!'

It was Kerry speaking unexpectedly and impulsively. She said more calmly:

'Don't go because of me, Steve. I . . . I'm glad to see you.'

Steve hesitated for a moment and then made up his mind. 'I'll go down and get your case,' he said quietly.

The moment he was gone, Joanna said: 'What is it, Kerry? A row?'

Kerry nodded, tears filling her eyes which she dashed away with her hands like a small girl.

'It's worse than that. I've left Luke. Jo, I don't know how to tell you. It . . . it's awful!'

Joanna fished a handkerchief from her handbag and tossed it over to Kerry.

'Let's have it quickly, Kerry, before Steve gets back. Just what has happened now— another woman?'

Kerry shook her head and gave her cousin a wry smile.

'No, oddly enough. We'd been happy together for the last few weeks. I thought everything was fine, except that I haven't been feeling too well. Yesterday . . .' she shot Joanna a look filled with pain. 'Yesterday I went to the doctor. I'm having a baby, Jo.'

Joanna gasped. Then asked:

'But surely that's what you wanted?'

'I wanted it—yes!' Kerry's voice was bitter. 'But Luke doesn't. Jo, you can't imagine what it was like . . . when I told him, I mean. It reminded me of that day that girl came to the flat and told us she was having Luke's child, do you remember?'

Joanna turned away, hiding her expression from the younger girl. With Gemma Phillips's letter burning a hole in her handbag, she was not likely to have forgotten.

'At first Luke tried to make out it wasn't his. It . . . it was terrible, Jo . . . degrading. I think he knew all along it was. Then he told me he'd pay for me to get rid of it. When he realized I wouldn't consider such a thing, he said either he'd leave me or I could leave him—he wasn't having any kids around the place. I didn't know what to do . . . so I came here.'

'And a good thing, too,' Joanna said, putting

110

her arm round Kerry's shoulders and hugging her. 'What's more, you're going to stay with me. I wouldn't let you go back to that . . . that . . .'

'Joanna, don't. Luke can't help it.'

'Then he should bloody well be made to help it!' Joanna burst out, unable to stand hearing Kerry defend her husband after what he had done to her. 'Are we going to let Steve in on this?'

'Steve?' It was as if she had completely forgotten him. 'No, don't tell him. He might be upset. Please, don't put off your dinner with him because of me. Just so long as I can stay here I'll be all right.'

Joanna sat down beside Kerry and gripped her hand tightly.

'Kerry, you've simply got to face facts. You can't go on living in a dream world any longer. You've left Luke—for good, I hope. You're going to have a child. Those are the facts. And there's one more. Steve is still in love with you. Whatever happens to you affects him. I think he ought to know.'

'All right, if you think it best. But it can't really concern him, Joanna. What was between us is all over and finished with. I haven't seen Steve in six months or more.'

'I know. But he is still your friend . . . and you're going to need your friends now, Kerry, more than ever. Don't shut him out of your life.'

Kerry's eyes were full of tears again.

'I don't want to . . . but I thought I should. I don't love him, Jo . . . I love Luke.'

The door opened and Steve came in. If he had heard Kerry's words, he did not say so. Joanna stood up quickly and said:

'I think we'll all three go out to dinner. I'm starving and Kerry looks as if she could do with a good square meal. Can you manage two females, Steve?'

He grinned and nodded his head.

'Go into my room and freshen up, Kerry,' Joanna suggested. 'Steve and I will have another drink while we are waiting for you.'

Kerry disappeared obediently, and while she was gone, Joanna told him the news.

'Strange, isn't it?' she ended thoughtfully. 'Coming on top of Gemma Phillips's letter and our conversation about it. We're back to square one, aren't we? I'm no longer sure I should show her that letter. In fact, I think it might be about the last straw. Do you agree?'

Steve was fingering the stem of his glass, his face thoughtful and filled with uncertainty.

'No, I don't think she should see the letter. I'm worried, Joanna. What will happen, do you suppose. Kerry needs someone to look after her. She has you, but . . . well, I don't imagine you can afford to keep her and . . . and a child. Then there's the question of whether Austin will change his mind and want her back.'

Joanna gave a short laugh.

'That I do doubt—Kerry *and a child?* No, Steve! I think this is the end of that marriage. And it couldn't be ending more unfortunately as far as I can see. Why, oh, why, didn't she leave him after your trip to Italy. Now it's too late for her to make a fresh start.'

Steve was silent. Only as Joanna was speaking did he realize that after all these years of patient waiting, Kerry was within his reach; she needed him now as she had never needed him in the past. But it was no longer just Kerry—if he married her and she agreed to marry him, then he would have Luke Austin's child too. The idea horrified him. He had dreamed so often in the past of having children—his and Kerry's. But another man's child—and at that a man he couldn't stand. No, he couldn't do it. He'd help in every possible way but not that . . . he just couldn't bring himself to accept that . . .

He said quietly, almost apologetically:

'I bought that little cottage in the country . . . I suppose it was mad but at the time, there was still some hope in my mind that Kerry and I . . . anyway, I did buy it and it's still empty. Kerry could live there, rent free . . . with the child. And if she needed money . . . you've only got to let me know.'

Joanna looked at him thoughtfully. She knew exactly what Steve's offer meant. He couldn't bring himself to offer marriage but his love for Kerry was still sufficiently strong for

113

him to want to help her as far as he could. She felt like crying. She couldn't blame Steve. What man would want to take on another man's child—especially if it were a man like Luke Austin. Steve was human and the situation was tragic. It was highly improbable that Kerry would agree to having the baby adopted—in fact Joanna knew already that it wouldn't cross Kerry's mind.

'We'll talk it over some more—later!' she said gently. 'The next job is to try to get some good food into the girl. She looks half starved.'

Steve took them to a small Italian restaurant near by but despite their entreaties, Kerry ate practically nothing. The meal passed awkwardly with conversation forced and stilted. By mutual agreement, they packed it up early and Steve went home after dropping the two girls at Joanna's flat.

Joanna ran a hot bath for Kerry and tucked her into bed. Then she sat beside the girl and talked.

'Kerry, darling, will you please listen to me? And for once in your sweet young life, try to take my advice. You've got to give up your habit of "wait and see". If you're leaving Luke, there can be no going back on your decision. Is your mind made up about that?'

Kerry nodded.

'I haven't any alternative. Luke doesn't want the baby.'

'But you do? You're quite sure that you do,

Kerry?'

Again Kerry nodded. She looked suddenly to Joanna terribly young and vulnerable, sitting back in bed with her fair hair over her pale thin little face. She did not look to her cousin as if she were old enough or physically strong enough to go through with this.

'Yes, now that it has happened, I haven't any choice. I'd never, *never* try to get rid of it.'

'No, that would be wrong and dangerous. But Kerry, you could offer it for adoption.'

'Hand my child over to . . . to someone else?' Kerry's voice was shocked. 'I couldn't do that, Jo—not even for Luke.'

'Then I suppose you wouldn't consider it for Steve?'

Kerry frowned.

'For Steve? I don't understand.'

'Kerry, Steve loves you—he always has and I think he always will. He would marry you if you left Luke and wanted him as a husband. He'd make a good husband. Then in time there would be children of your own—yours and Steve's. He'd look after you and . . .'

'No, Jo!' Kerry broke in sharply. 'I don't love Steve and even if I did, I wouldn't have him at that price. I won't give up my baby—not to anyone.'

'Steve wouldn't take Luke's child . . .'

'I don't want him to. Jo, why keep on about Steve? This has nothing to do with him.'

'It has, Kerry. He loves you. Anything that

happens to you has its repercussion on him. He wants to help now. Oh, my dear, I wish you could be less romantic and more practical about life. Can't you understand that life isn't going to be easy for you—a divorced woman with a child. It isn't as if Luke has money. You'll get a third of his income, of course, and an allowance for the baby. That is, if he pays up and from what I know of Luke Austin, I think you might have trouble getting money from him regularly. He won't want to pay. And it isn't as if he has a salary. He can sell his pictures and declare to the court that he only got a few pounds for them.'

'I don't want his money!' Kerry cried. 'I can work, can't I?'

'With a baby to look after? There are a good many unmarried mothers who have tried it, Kerry, and found it pretty difficult.'

'You're asking me to give up the child?' Joanna looked away from those questioning, shocked eyes. She said quietly:

'Not to do it but to consider it, Kerry. And to consider Steve just a little. You told me you thought you could have been quite happy married to Steve—if you hadn't ever met Luke. I think so, too. He has been utterly faithful and constant and he loves you far, far more than Luke Austin could ever love anyone. Think about a future *with* Steve.'

'I couldn't—I can't. *I don't love him.*'

'Does that matter?' Joanna asked pointedly.

'Where has love got you, Kerry? There are hundreds of marriages every day that begin with friendship and end happily. You *like* Steve and he's absolutely right for you. You enjoy being together—you even enjoyed sleeping together. What more do you want?'

For a moment Kerry was silent. Then she said so softly that Joanna had to strain to hear the words.

'I want Luke's baby. I want to keep my child.'

CHAPTER SIX

Despite everything Joanna might say, Steve was appalled by his reaction to Kerry's coming child. He felt that he ought to be able to detach himself from those twin feelings of jealousy and repulsion. Love, he told himself, if worth anything at all, should make it possible for him to put aside such paltry emotions in favour of the much greater joy of making Kerry his wife; of accepting the child, giving it his name and thereby giving Kerry the security and love she so desperately needed.

'Don't torment yourself, Steve. It's all perfectly understandable. No man in your position would want to start a marriage on such a foundation. It isn't as if you liked Luke Austin. Moreover, we both heartily dislike him. It is therefore more than understandable if you don't want to adopt his child. I should be much more surprised if you did.'

They were sitting in the tiny drawing room of Kerry's cottage in Sussex—Steve's cottage, really, but he had had the lease put in her name when she had moved there three months ago. Kerry was at work now—earning herself a meagre eight pounds a week typing in the local office of Steve's estate agency. She would be back on the five-thirty bus and had given Steve her key so that he could let Joanna in when she arrived for a weekend visit. Steve had stayed to have a cup of tea with Kerry's cousin and to discuss the situation.

In answer to Jo's remark, Steve said quietly:

'Some men have done just that, Joanna. But somehow, I can't bring myself to feel anything but an acute antipathy for her child. Maybe I subconsciously blame it for coming between Kerry and me. If it were not for this baby, she might have left Luke Austin and married me.'

Jo lit a cigarette and looked at the burning tip with a thoughful expression.

'On the other hand, Steve, if it hadn't been for the baby, Kerry would still be living with Luke. You've got to remember that. And how do you know she would have married you even if she had left him for some other reason?'

Steve flinched.

'Okay, I know that's a fair comment. I don't even know if Kerry would marry me now. It would be just like her to refuse simply because she would feel she was taking advantage of the situation.'

'You haven't discussed it with her?'

Steve shook his head.

'Somehow Kerry always manages to keep our conversation strictly impersonal. We never mention love—Luke—the baby.'

Jo smiled.

'Then what do you talk about?'

'This cottage. Kerry loves it. She has made it very nice, don't you agree? In fact, it's so comfortable and attractive, I always have a job to tear myself away. We discuss money . . . Kerry insists on paying me a token pound a week rent. I always try to refuse it but she is quite adamant. Frankly, I don't know how she is managing. I know she is putting money aside—presumably for the baby's birth and after. It can't leave her much over for fuel, food, clothes and fares. I wish I could persuade her to let me help—but of course, she won't even discuss it.'

'I know! The one time I tried to slip her a cheque, she all but blew the roof off,' Joanna agreed. 'Kerry's proud, Steve, and so long as she *can* manage, I think we should let her do so.'

Steve paced the tiny floor restlessly.

'She must be so lonely here all by herself. I hate to think of her here alone at night. The cottage is very isolated—it could even be dangerous . . . but she swears she doesn't mind. Of course, I drop in whenever I can and I know you're down every other weekend—but . . . well, it's not much of a life, is it? Kerry won't come out with me. She said that because we're obvious friends, people might start gossiping about whose baby it really is!'

'Pride again!' was Jo's comment. 'I suppose it's the reaction from her life with Luke which must have been one long humiliation. Thank God that marriage is finally over. I suppose you know divorce proceedings are in progress? Luke is divorcing Kerry for adultery and she isn't defending it. Of course, she could have used Gemma Phillips as evidence to divorce him, but I couldn't make her do that. She says she prefers to be the so-called "guilty party" rather than bring that poor girl into the picture.'

'You didn't tell Kerry about the letter, then?'

'No! I saw no point in it. I wrote to the girl explaining that Kerry was having a child of her own so what she had asked was out of the question. As a matter of fact, I sent her another cheque—because I realized Kerry would have wanted to help if she could. I've not heard again. I don't suppose we shall hear any more now. No doubt she's had *her* baby adopted.'

If only Kerry would do that!'

The words were out before Steve could stop

them. Joanna looked at him compassionately.

'I'm afraid that can't happen, Steve. Kerry's whole life centres round the baby now. It's as if she can bring herself to live without Luke now she has part of him which will belong to her always. Don't worry so much about her, Steve. I don't think she is unhappy.'

Steve was silent. He, too, did not believe that Kerry was actively unhappy. In fact, she seemed far less emotionally overwrought than she had been for years. Her face had filled out and she had put on weight which greatly improved her looks. She looked younger, sweeter, more composed. Her approaching motherhood had given her a new kind of dignity which puzzled him even while it kept him at bay.

One of the things he could not tell even Joanna, was that Kerry's physical shape, now that she was in the sixth month, embarrassed and unnerved him. Perhaps Kerry was conscious of this for she tried to conceal her size beneath loose-fitting garments; succeeding so well that he would forget about it until he saw her walk across a room or stoop awkwardly to retrieve something from the floor. Then he would remember and avoid her eyes until he forgot again. She never flaunted her pregnancy as he had seen other women do, but he guessed that this was not because she was in any way ashamed but out of respect for his feelings.

Being in Kerry's company now did not bring him any real happiness. He was too hardly besieged by a persistent feeling of guilt towards her and of failure in himself. His love ought to be strong enough to overcome this particular emotional barrier yet it was not. In fact, when it had come to the first severe test, it had crawled shame-facedly into a corner to hide itself. Not that he had ceased to love her—but he now knew that this Great Passion was a far weaker thing than he had believed it to be and certainly not much to offer Kerry. Instead, he gave her his friendship and help, providing her with a home and a job and visiting her regularly with little presents of flowers or chocolates which were all she would accept.

He had, too, cut the grass in the garden and planted some rose trees and in return, Kerry had cooked meals for him and made him a welcome and comfortable guest. Their life seemed to have become more or less completely domesticated—in fact, they might almost have been married except that he had never once kissed her, touched her or spoken of his feelings.

This strange relationship appeared to satisfy Kerry and, Steve was forced to admit, was in itself satisfying to him, too. If it could have continued like this, there would be no problem for he could think of nothing he wanted more than to spend his days quietly in this pretty

122

little cottage with Kerry for company. But he was as aware as Kerry of the approaching date of her child's birth. Upstairs, in the room next to Kerry's, were a carri-cot and bath and a little chest of drawers (which he himself had painted lemon and white) stacked with baby clothes. She had been too sensitive to call this a nursery; had merely answered his request for a job of work one wet day with the tentative suggestion that he re-decorate the 'spare room'. But Steve had known it was for the baby and he dreaded its arrival; wondering if he could continue to come here as he now did, most days of the week. He could not ignore an existing child the way he could ignore it now. He would hear it cry; have to watch Kerry attending to its needs when he called round. And he was by no means sure if he could hide his aversion.

Steve sighed and gave his attention back to Joanna. He had grown very fond of this cousin of Kerry's. And what a marvellous friend she had turned out to be to Kerry. Steve could well understand why she adored Joanna. Beneath the rather frivolous exterior, Jo was so very *sensible*. He appealed to her now, saying:

'If you were me, Joanna, would you behave differently?'

Joanna smiled.

'I suppose by that you mean, would I ask Kerry to marry me. The answer is, of course, no. She has already suffered quite enough

123

from one marriage which tore her emotionally in two. For you to marry her now feeling as you do about Luke's child would be repeating the mental torture for her. It is far better this way, Steve. She has you for a friend, and in that she is very lucky.'

He knew Joanna was right but words, even while they confirmed his own views, could not lessen his feelings of inadequacy.

'I'd better get along,' he said, sighing. 'Kerry will be here any moment and she is sure to want a nice girlish gossip alone with you. Maybe you and Kerry would lunch with me at the pub tomorrow? If Kerry agrees.'

'I'd love that, Steve—and I'm sure she would,' Joanna thanked him and walked with him to the door.

His car had barely rounded the corner of the lane before Kerry came walking up the flagged path and threw herself into Joanna's arms, her face a big warm welcome.

'It's lovely to see you, Jo. I've been longing for this weekend. Have you had a drink? Steve let you in? Yes, of course, he has!'

She took off her coat and flung it over the back of a chair and turned to find Jo's eyes on her. She smiled, patting her tummy ruefully.

'I'm a size, aren't I? I'm sure I shouldn't be so big yet. I asked Dr. Mason if I was having twins but apparently not!'

'Heaven forbid!' Jo said. 'One will be quite enough to look after. Tell me, Kerry, are you

124

intending to keep on your job after the baby's arrival?'

Kerry sat down with difficulty into one of the armchairs and stretched out her legs luxuriously.

'I'll have to work, Jo. And Steve has very kindly offered to keep my job open. I've made some inquiries and the farmer's wife who lives about half a mile from here will look after the baby during working hours. She only wants thirty shillings a week, so it's all fixed up. But I'm having two whole months off—a couple of weeks before and six weeks after. In a minute, when I can shift myself, I'll take you up to see the baby's room. I've got some lovely little things for him, Jo . . .'

Her cousin listened as Kerry prattled happily and maternally about her preparations. It was good to see her so relaxed and content. The tortured expression had left her face which was now calm and happy. Was it life apart from Luke which produced this change? Or merely nature making the expectant mother placid? Jo hoped it was the former— otherwise Kerry might suffer from a feeling of anti-climax after the baby's arrival; realize just what a load she had chosen to carry, bringing up a child by herself; trying to run a home, be a mother and work at the same time.

It was only much later, after they had had supper and were drinking coffee in front of the fire that Kerry suddenly spoke of Luke. She said:

'I saw Luke the other day—in Selfridges.'

'To speak to?' Joanna asked, her curiosity aroused. Not that she had any interest at all in Luke Austin, but she wondered how the meeting had affected Kerry.

'Yes! We were both in the coffee bar, I'd been up to buy some cot blankets in the sale. I don't know what Luke was doing there. He was with a girl.'

Although she was watching Kerry's face closely, Joanna could see no change in her expression.

'You went over and spoke to him?'

Kerry shook her head.

'No! He came over to me. You know, Jo, he really is a rather extraordinary person. He spoke to me as if nothing whatever had happened and there were no divorce proceedings in progress; in fact, as if we were old friends and had never been married. He was really quite pleasant—asked me where I was living; how I could stick a nine-to-five job; whether I found being pregnant a bore.'

Jo flushed.

'He's got a nerve . . .' she began indignantly, but Kerry broke in softly:

'You just don't understand Luke as I do. He has mentally dissociated himself from the past but that doesn't mean he bears me any ill-will or that he expects me to bear him any ill-will either.'

126

'For heaven's sake, Kerry—it is *his* child.'

'Luke doesn't believe that. He says it is Steve's!'

Joanna's face flushed an even deeper red. 'How could he think that. It's outrageous . . .'

Kerry's face silenced her.

It's not really—after all, I did go away with Steve and although there is no question of the baby being Steve's, it could have happened that I was having his child. Luke knows I was unfaithful to him and he prefers to think some other man is responsible. That's all.'

'That's all!' Joanna repeated, unable to keep the sarcasm from her voice.

'Well, it might have happened, Jo, so I've no right to take such a moral tone, have I? I did wrong going away with Steve and I know it. You know, of the hopeless mess I've made of my life, Steve is the one person I'm sorriest for. He's the one who has been most hurt—not Luke—he doesn't care; not me—I have the baby; but Steve. He's lost everything.'

'Oh, Kerry, you are a hopeless case—you are the victim, darling, not Steve. Why, Steve could marry you if he wanted to, couldn't he? No one is stopping him except himself.'

'But that's not true—Luke's child is stopping him. He can't bear the thought of it, Jo, and it hurts him terribly every time he remembers it.'

Jo was silent, thoughtful, as she stared into the fire.

'Do you love Steve, Kerry?'

'Yes, I do. But not in the way you mean, Jo. I love him in much the same way as I love you—that means a very deep affection, bound up with gratitude and understanding and respect. I am not "in love" if by that one means what I felt for Luke. That was something quite beyond my control—a compulsion. When I saw Luke in London, I looked at him and knew I would never be able to feel that way again with or about another man.'

'But, Kerry, you couldn't ever *respect* Luke.'

'No, I suppose not. But I love him and it's useless asking me why. I can't even answer the question.'

'Still?'

'I suppose so. The strange thing is that since the baby became real to me I've not wanted anything else. Physical love is unimportant to me. I seem quite numb to that side of life. I suppose Steve guesses this—or else it is because he feels the same way. At any rate, that side of our relationship has ceased to exist. Yet once it was important to me.'

'And might be again—after the child is born!' Jo said warningly. 'This may be only a temporary reaction, Kerry. Are you going to be able to lead the rest of your life in that way? I doubt it.'

Again Kerry smiled.

'I'll worry about that when it happens.

Somehow I can't bring myself to be worried about anything right now, Jo. Life is satisfactory as it is. My only complaint is that time passes slowly and it sometimes seems as if the nine months will never come to an end. But at other times, I want this contentment and excitement I feel to go on for ever. I'm happy, Jo—for the first time in years.'

'You look it!' Joanna admitted, staring at Kerry's bright eyes and unlined face. In fact, her young cousin looked positively beautiful.

She wished she could rid herself of her fears for the future. Kerry seemingly had none—so why should she worry about the unknown tomorrow? Maybe Kerry would find fulfilment in her child. Many women did. She was clearly a far more maternal type than Joanna had supposed. She could now visualize Kerry, married to Steve, with half a dozen children running round the place . . .

'You won't go back to Luke, will you?' she asked into the silence and was relieved when Kerry shook her head.

'No, I'll never go back. Luke wouldn't want me and I wouldn't want to go. That's all over, Jo. I've started a new life here and I like it. I'm happy. Don't worry so much about me, you chump!'

But although she returned Kerry's smile, Joanna felt a continuing premonition of disaster. It was as if a warning voice deep down inside her mind was telling her that her young cousin's placid contentment could not possibly last.

'A born pessimist,' she told herself sharply. But knew that it was not so. By nature, she looked on the bright side of life. Why, then, was she so sure that Kerry, who had already suffered so much, should have further pain to endure?

CHAPTER SEVEN

Kerry was happy. There were, of course, moments when this was not altogether true; for instance, when Jo went back to London after a weekend visit. Then the cottage would seem strangely quiet and Kerry would be conscious of loneliness. But this did not last for long. Monday morning meant work again and in Steve's office there were other people to talk to, even if none of the young men and women who worked with her were exactly her friends. They knew she was there because of Steve and despite Steve's easy way with his employees, he was still the boss and Kerry the boss's friend.

She took care always to treat Steve formally when she saw him at work. She never asked for privileges or took time off even when Steve suggested it. She worked as hard and as well as she could, determined to earn her salary. She

130

quite liked the work although now she had begun to feel a certain amount of backache from sitting upright at her desk for long hours at a time, typing or checking house particulars. It was always a relief to get home. Of late, she had appreciated more than ever Steve's help around the cottage. He did all the heavy chores for her, managing the boiler and getting in enough coal and logs to last her until he was next there.

Her relationship with him was completely satisfactory to her, except for one factor—that she felt it was not as good for him. He had become, for her, the kindly elder brother who looked after her; upon whom she could depend for help and advice and whose companionship she enjoyed and valued. This transference from boy friend to platonic companion had been easy enough for her. Since leaving Luke, she had lost all desire for physical contact with any man. In fact, it was as if all emotion had died inside her and been replaced by her quiet steady joy in approaching motherhood. The baby was everything now; her reason for living, her whole happiness. She loved being with Steve or Jo, her two best friends, but the most important thing in her life was the child she carried inside her.

She understood and respected Steve's aversion to her pregnancy. Sadly, she recognized that if it had been *his* child she was carrying, it would have been an equal joy to him. Sometimes she would worry over the future—whether Steve would wish to spend so much time with her once the baby had arrived. She knew it might mean an end to their companionship and the thought made her sad. But she never wished her situation otherwise.

Of Luke she thought very seldom. Only occasionally, when she was lying in bed in the dark unable to sleep, her mind would turn to her husband; to the strange meeting when he had come over to her to talk in that casual, impersonal way as if they had been old friends rather than a husband and wife in the process of being divorced. Even now she could not hate him. Luke was Luke and it was useless to think that he might have behaved differently. His reactions should have been known to her at once and she had been stupid in hoping he would welcome his child. As if Luke would welcome any responsibilities or ties! Perhaps it was all much better this way. Now she could give all her time, love and attention to the baby.

There was no room for pleasure—only for an incredulous surprise, when she returned from work one evening to find her husband sitting on a suitcase by the front door. She paused on the pathway, staring at him open-mouthed, unable to believe her own eyes.

'Well, don't stand there staring at me as if I were a ghost!'

Luke's voice was anything but dreamlike. It held the well-remembered note of irritation and impatience. 'I've been waiting nearly an hour and I'm frozen stiff.'

She took a few steps towards him, still unable to believe that Luke had come down here to visit her.

'Do you have to lock, bar and bolt everything? Even the bathroom window was tight shut!' Luke went on, swinging his arms against his sides to restore the circulation. 'Damn it all, Kerry, I haven't even got an overcoat.'

She noticed then that he was in the inevitable jeans and thick polo-necked sweater, neither any too clean, stained here and there with oil paint.

'I'm so sorry, Luke. If I'd known you were coming . . .'

She broke off, fumbling for her key. It never occurred to her to refuse to let him in, or to be surprised when he walked past her into the tiny hallway, without waiting, as Steve would have done, for her to go in first.

'My God, it's cold! Where's the fireplace?'

He found his way into the sitting-room and stirred some smouldering logs so that they burst into flame.

'That's better. Let's have some light.'

Kerry touched the switch and the room was at once warm-looking and welcoming. Luke looked round him appreciatively.

133

'Nice place! Made it quite home-like, haven't you?' His voice was not sarcastic but held its derisive note as if he thought there was something suburban in being comfortable.

Kerry found her voice.

'I'll make some tea,' she said. Her heart was pounding uneasily in her chest and below, she felt the child kick. Luke said:

'My God, can't I have something stronger than that!'

She felt the old familiar sense of inadequacy.

'I'm awfully sorry, Luke. I don't drink myself and there's only a little gin which Jo didn't finish last weekend.'

Luke was not a gin drinker—he preferred brandy.

'Well, that's better than tea,' he commented, and sank into the armchair by the fire, leaning forward to throw on two more logs now that those in the grate had kindled.

For a second, Kerry stood in the doorway staring at that sharp handsome profile. Her random thoughts pondered whether in fact Luke's child would look like him. Then as he turned to stare at her impatiently, she swung round and went quickly into the kitchen to find the drink.

When she returned, Luke was completely at ease in front of the fire. He had removed his shoes and looked comfortable and very much at home. He took the glass and looked at her

134

over the rim.

'Quite a size, aren't you, my Katriona? I hadn't noticed it beneath your coat. When's the happy day?'

To her annoyance she found herself blushing. For the first time, she was embarrassed by her pregnancy. She sat down slowly and said:

'There's still a couple of months to wait . . .'

Luke made no reply. There was a small, enigmatic smile on his face. Presently, he looked up at her again and said:

'You do live here alone, then?'

Again, Kerry felt herself blushing.

'Of course!' she said.

Luke laughed.

'Yes! It would be "of course" with you. I had wondered if that Stephen bloke was living with you. It's his cottage, isn't it?'

'I pay him rent!' Kerry said quickly.

'More fool you!' Luke said laughing. 'Well, that's your affair. I'm glad you aren't living with him.'

Curiosity forced her into the question. 'Why?'

'Well, it would have made it a bit awkward for me, wouldn't it?'

Kerry frowned.

'I don't understand. You mean because of the divorce . . . ?'

'Good God, no!' Luke broke in. 'The divorce has nothing to do with it. As a matter of fact, I'm calling off proceedings.'

'Calling off . . . but I don't understand. What are you trying to say, Luke?'

'I am saying it, if you'll only listen. I've decided not to divorce you after all. That's simple enough, isn't it?'

'Yes, but why? What's happened?'

Luke's expression darkened. His mouth hardened.

'Well, I can't very well divorce you and live with you at the same time, can I? Not exactly the done thing, I imagine.'

This time, Kerry was too shaken to reply. Her mind seemed unable to comprehend what Luke was saying. He wanted to live here, with her. It didn't make sense.

'Don't look so staggered, Katriona!' Luke's voice was soft now and faintly teasing. 'Don't you want me here?'

'I don't know!' The truth came out before she could consider the question. Did she want Luke here? Hadn't she found herself far more content without him? And yet . . . *why* did he want to come back? Had the impossible happened and Luke found that after all he was really in love with her? That he wanted his child?

'Oh, come on, Kerry. Don't tell me you've fallen out of love with me.'

Pride stung her to reply:

'And why not?'

'Simply that you still cared all right when I

saw you last month in town. And don't try to deny it—I saw it in your eyes when I came over to talk to you.'

Kerry was silent. What was there to say? It was only too true that the unexpected sight of Luke had shaken her—would always have the power to disturb her. Even now, she was trembling, although it was most probably due to the series of shocks he had given her.

'So here I am. I trust you aren't going to throw the errant husband out?'

'I don't know . . . I don't know if I do want you here. I've got used to living alone. I . . . I just don't understand all this . . . it doesn't make sense. You'll have to give me time to think it out, Luke.'

'Can't do that!' Luke said laconically. 'Last bus went ten minutes ago. Which reminds me, I left my suitcase outside. Better get it in, I suppose.'

'No, Luke . . .' Her voice trailed away as he stood up and touched the top of her head with one long slim white hand.

'Such pretty, pretty hair!' he said softly. 'I'd forgotten your pretty hair.'

Tears suddenly stung her eyes. Luke tender and loverlike was so rare a thing—so mesmerizing. She could no longer think sensibly. The only important thing in the world was the feel of his hand gently stroking her head.

'Love me a little bit?' His voice was low,

husky. 'I know I've been all sorts of a swine but I'll try to be better in future. You do want me back, don't you, my Katriona? You need someone to look after you. It isn't right for you to be alone.'

She turned suddenly and looked up into his face. There was a faint smile in his eyes as he looked back at her. Only his mouth was not smiling but looked vaguely cruel and determined. She felt a combination of fear and excitement. Then, as he allowed the smile to cover all his face, she relaxed and said weakly:

'I suppose now you are here and the bus has gone . . .'

'That's right. That's my sensible Katriona. I'll get my case and then we'll find something to eat.'

Once he was out of the room, some of his hypnotic influence over her went with him. She was suddenly afraid again. None of this made sense. Why was Luke here? It just wasn't possible that he had suddenly felt a need to be with her; or, as he had declared, a desire to look after her. It wasn't like Luke to behave this way, and yet, wasn't it absolutely typical of him to do the unexpected . . .

Her thoughts roamed feverishly to Joanna—how angry and upset her cousin would be. Maybe Luke didn't intend to stay long. Maybe he was just running away from some persistent girl in town who . . . Steve would be here soon—in an hour at the most.

He would be horrified to find Luke here. Poor Steve . . .

'There we are! I'll unpack later. What's for supper? I hope you've got something to eat. I'm starving.'

'Luke!' She stood up, her voice determined. 'I think you owe me an explanation. I have to know why you are here.'

'Why shouldn't I be here?'

'There is no reason why not, I suppose. But I feel there must be a reason why. I want to know.' She was pleading with him now.

'Don't be a bore, Kat. Surely the reason is obvious. I just got fed up living in the studio. I wanted to be with you. I thought of you living down here alone in the country and it seemed the obvious thing to do—to come here and live with you. After all, we are married.' He gave a short laugh. 'Funny, really, when you think about it.'

'Luke, you haven't forgotten that I'm having a baby?'

'Forgotten! That's hardly possible, my love, with you the size you are. So what? As long as you keep it out of my way, I don't care. I think I could work here—get some real painting done. Is there a barn or something I could turn into a decent studio? This room hasn't enough light. What about an attic? Is there an attic, Kerry?'

'I don't know . . . oh, Luke . . .' She was unsure whether to laugh or cry. It might be a long, long time before Luke could be happy about his child, but at least he was no longer set against it. Now, like a miracle, the impossible had happened. He was back of his own free will and they were going to start life together again.

A warning voice inside her told her to be careful. Luke's improbable arrival out of the blue was like a miracle, but he might just as easily walk out again. She must be prepared— steel herself against taking him or his love for granted. She must understand from this moment that there could never be any security. It was up to her to decide whether to accept this, enjoy happiness, however brief, and then accept the hurt if he went; or to refuse it altogether.

But there was no doubt in her mind. She could not refuse it. Whatever his motives, Luke needed her, wanted her and wanted to live here with her and the baby.

She felt a sudden rush of gladness that she had insisted on paying Steve rent for the cottage. If it had been his house she was living in, then she could not have let Luke stay here. But she was free of financial obligation to Steve—free to have Luke back in her life . . .

'I'll get a meal,' she said quickly, happily. 'There are two chops in the fridge and I know I've a tin of mushrooms . . .'

Luke let out his breath. Until this moment, he had not felt a hundred per cent sure of his welcome. Now he knew Kerry had accepted him.

'Sounds fine!' he said agreeably. 'While you're getting it, I'm going to have another snifter of cousin Jo's gin.'

Kerry realized as she dished up the meal fifteen minutes later, that Luke was a little tight. He'd probably had no lunch and the three gins had gone into an empty stomach. He tucked into the food ravenously and did not notice that she ate nothing. Excitement, shock and a sudden unexpected fatigue, had destroyed her appetite. She persuaded him to eat her chop as well as his own and watched him enjoying it.

'You always were a good cook!' he complimented her. 'Remember the *chile con carne you* used to make?'

'I couldn't eat that now!' Kerry smiled back at him. 'The seasoning would give me frantic indigestion.'

For a moment, he looked puzzled and then he said:

'I forgot the little bastard!'

'Luke!' Her voice was shocked.

'Okay, okay—sorry for the bad language.'

'Luke, please don't joke about the baby. It—it's very important to me. I don't expect you to feel the same way—but if we are going to live together again, you've got to understand how I feel about it.'

Luke's reply was unconcerned.

'I said I was sorry. Don't get so worked up. You always were so intense. Calm down, my love, and relax.'

She sat back, suddenly uneasy. Luke was right—she was tensed up in a way she hadn't felt for months. Why should being with him have the power to do this to her? He hadn't meant to be offensive. She must learn to accept his casual way of speaking. It was so easy to forget how different Luke was from other men . . . Steve, for instance, Steve would never have talked that way . . .

Steve!

'He'll be here in a minute!' she gasped. 'I should have telephoned and told him not to come.'

'Who?' Luke's voice was sharp.

'Steve. He was coming round for coffee and then he was going to put another shelf for me in the spare room.'

'Well, okay, why get in a tizzy about that. I'm not going to eat him.'

'But, Luke, he . . . he won't be pleased to see *you.*'

'So what?' Luke shrugged his shoulders. 'He can always push off if he can't stand my company. Anyway, why won't he be pleased to see me?'

'Because he is still in love with me.' But she did not say the words aloud. Reading her silence, Luke laughed.

'The faithful admirer still hoping!' he said

sarcastically. 'High time you let him off the hook, Katriona—unless, of course, you do intend to marry him eventually?'

Kerry flushed.

'I'm not keeping him on the hook. In any case, he doesn't want to marry me . . . he's just a very good friend. I wouldn't want him upset. He's been very good to me, Luke.'

'Okay, so I'll be nice and polite and welcoming. Why, you're trembling, Kerry. What in heaven's name is the matter with you?'

'I just don't feel like a scene. Luke, promise you won't say anything to upset him. Steve will behave, I know, so long as you do. Please, Luke. I don't want to lose my job for one thing . . . I work in Steve's firm.'

Luke's eyes narrowed.

'Do you now? Well, why didn't you say so right off? I'll certainly not bite the hand that feeds us, so cheer up, Kat, and get some coffee going. I feel just the littlest bit woozy.'

Alone in the kitchen, Kerry's confidence departed once more. Steve was going to be horrified, finding Luke here. If only she could have warned him.

But as if on cue, the door knocker went rat-ta-ta-tat-tat, Steve's signal.

It was impossible to run in her condition, but she hurried into the hall, her heart thudding painfully. She opened the door and Steve smiled at her and said:

'Sorry if I'm a bit late . . . how are you, Kerry? You look a bit tired. May I come in?'

She realized then that she had been blocking the doorway; she stood back to let him come into the hall. He took off his heavy overcoat. As he hung it up, he caught sight of Luke's suitcase.

'Why didn't you tell me, Kerry?'

His voice was quite normal, friendly.

'Tell you!' she repeated stupidly.

'That Joanna was here? I never realized she . . .'

'Steve, it isn't Jo, it's . . . Luke!'

'Luke!' He could not have looked more astonished. He stared down at her disbelievingly. 'Luke! You mean your husband?'

Kerry nodded her head.

'But I don't understand—you didn't say . . .'

'Come into the kitchen!' Kerry broke in quickly. 'Please, Steve. Luke's in the sitting-room.'

He followed her into the kitchen and stood leaning against the doorframe, his face bewildered and questioning.

'I didn't know he was coming, Steve. When I got home from work he was here, waiting for me. He . . . he wants to stay and . . . well, I've said he can.'

Steve's voice was rough with sudden anger.

'You must be mad!'

She was pleading with him, fighting against

144

his disapproval.

'He is my husband!'

'And a bloody awful husband he's been, too. Well, I'd better push off.'

She caught his arm and said nervously:

'No, don't go. Please don't go. Luke knows you're coming for coffee and he doesn't mind—he . . . he wants to be friends. Please don't go, Steve. I want you to stay!'

Something of the fear she was not even conscious of herself penetrated to the man standing near her. It was as if Kerry had been pleading with him for protection of some kind. Could that brute of a husband have threatened her in some way?

'Then you will stay!' She took his hesitation for acceptance and gave a quick, nervous smile. 'I've just made the coffee—I'll bring it in.'

In a few moments while she collected cups and saucers and put them on a tray, Steve tried to recover from the shock she had given him. His uppermost feeling was one of acute resentment. Luke Austin had no damn right to burst in on Kerry's privacy in this way—he'd forfeited that right when he had denied his own child.

'What about the divorce?' he asked abruptly.

Kerry kept her back turned to him.

'He's dropping proceedings!' she said quietly. Then she turned and saw the expression on his face and cried: 'Don't look like that, Steve. Luke's changed—you'll see in a minute. He . . . he has asked me to have him back—I couldn't refuse.'

'Couldn't you?' The question was on his lips but he bit it back, knowing he had no right to utter the words. For months now he had believed that Kerry had ceased to be in love with her husband; that she had at last come to her senses and realized what a mistake she had made marrying the man. Now he was suddenly confronted with the appalling fact that Kerry was still in love with Luke.

'Come on, Steve!' She was waiting for him to follow her. Automatically, he took the tray from her—he wouldn't allow her to carry anything when he was with her. She led the way into the sitting-room and a voice from the armchair nearest the fire said:

'Wasn't that the boyfriend? Thought I heard the door knocker!'

'Luke!' Kerry's voice was sharp, embarrassed. Luke sat up and glanced over his shoulder, smiling sardonically. He made no effort to get up. He said:

'Oh, so I was right. Come and sit down, old chap. What's it like out, freezing?'

With an enormous effort of will, Steve refrained from walking over and smashing his fist into the man's face. For Kerry's sake only, he was willing to try to behave with decorum.

He put down the tray but stood until Kerry,

herself, was seated. He was aware of Luke's eyes on him, measuring him, no doubt.

'Have a gin?' he asked. 'It's all my Katriona has to offer, I'm afraid. You look as if you could do with a snifter!'

Steve shook his head, unable to trust his voice. Despite himself, he had felt a furious jealousy at Luke's possessive pronoun. 'My' Katriona! And the damnable part about it was that it was true—true . . .

He saw Kerry's eyes on him, enormous, seeming to plead with him to be polite to Luke—not to spoil this meeting. He said coldly:

'How's the painting?'

Luke stretched his legs and hunched his shoulders and grinned.

'Not so good, I'm afraid. The rush for modern art seems to have cooled off a bit.' He looked from Steve's face to Kerry's and said softly: 'Or maybe I've been missing my inspiration since my wife left me. I have a feeling that I might be able to do some good work here. Cosy, isn't it?' He stressed the word so that it sounded as if he was sneering at the comfort and security of the cottage.

'I love it here!' Kerry's voice was quick, eager, as if she were relieved to be on safe ground. She went on: 'It's been great fun doing it up. Steve has been a wonderful help—he put up those book shelves last weekend.'

'A Do-It-Yourself expert!' Again Luke's

147

voice held that faint note of derision. 'Kerry certainly lands on her feet, doesn't she? I mean, not every woman has her own handy-man to hand!' He laughed at his own words and poured himself the last of Joanna's gin.

Steve turned to Kerry.

'I can't stay long. I promised to be home for a long distance phone call at nine-thirty.'

They both knew he was lying. Luke, if he guessed, did not care. He said hospitably:

'You must come again soon, old boy. Drop in whenever you want. I gather it's your place, anyway. I'm sure Kerry will be glad of your company—I shall probably be busy most of the while painting.'

Steve put down his coffee cup and rose to his feet. He could not meet Kerry's eyes. Only with the greatest effort of will could he hold out his hand to her saying:

'I'd really better be getting along; I'll see you tomorrow, Kerry—at the office. Goodnight, Luke!'

Luke remained sitting. Kerry followed Steve out into the hall. Her face looked white, strained, miserable.

'He doesn't mean to be rude!' she whispered.

Steve's face twisted.

'Maybe not. But he ruddy well succeeds. Goodnight, Kerry. Look after yourself.'

She looked cumbersome, bulky, filling the tiny hall with her size. Only her face was beautiful—like a pale, tormented angel. Unable to bear it, Steve bent suddenly and kissed her gently. He said again, as if to reassure her:

'I'll see you tomorrow, Kerry.'

Then he was gone.

Kerry waited by the closed door until she heard his car driving off. She felt drained, exhausted, as if she had just witnessed some terrible accident in which she was powerless to do anything but stand by and watch. With Steve's going, all the warmth and security was gone, too. She was half afraid to rejoin Luke in the sitting-room and yet strangely excited by the thought that he was there.

Luke was still in his chair. He was smoking the last of the cigarettes in the box on the table beside him. He leant forward and kicked one of the logs further into the fire.

'He's got it bad, hasn't he?'

She was too tired to understand his meaning.

'The boyfriend! He's mad about you. Maybe you're sorry I'm not divorcing you after all, eh?' He reached out his arm and caught her hand and pulled her over to his chair, so that she was forced to look at him. 'Well? Do you want to be free so you can marry him? Or do you still love me?'

She tried to pull away, sensing that he was taunting her. His eyes looked cruel and yet his next words belied that cruelty:

'There's never been another woman in my life who has meant what you mean to me, Katriona. And God knows I've known enough women! Maybe I'm growing old—maybe I'll settle down now and make you a good husband. What about that, my love? Do you want me back? Really want me?'

'Luke, it isn't just a matter of . . . of you and me, now. There's the child—your child. In another few weeks it will exist. You say you want to settle down—to be a good husband. But are you willing to be a father, too? I'd never part with my baby—never, not even for you!'

He dropped her hand and stared down into the fire.

'Hell, I know that. I'm not blind, you know, Kat. One can hardly ignore the fact that you're pregnant! But you haven't heard me bitching about it, have you? I haven't said that if I stay, the kid's got to go.'

'Then you accept it? You admit that it is yours?'

'Don't be such a fool, Kat. Of course I know it's mine. Do you think I'd be here if I'd thought it was your boyfriend's? Besides, you'd have been marrying *him* if it was.'

'Oh, Luke!' She felt choked, unable to find words to express how she felt. If his words had been gentle, sentimental, loving, she might not have believed him so readily, but this was so like the Luke she knew that she could not doubt his sincerity. He needed her—just as once she had prayed so hard for him to need her. She could live without the endearments, the outward trappings of love, just so long as she knew for certain deep down inside that he did care, did want her, did need her. And now, like a miracle, her prayers had come true; she had even more than she had dared to hope for since Luke was willing to accept and acknowledge his child.

'Funny girl!' Luke said sleepily. 'Funny, strange, faithful Katriona.'

She wondered suddenly if he was drunk; but unable to bear the suspicion, she shut her eyes and caught his hand and held it firmly but tenderly against her cheek.

CHAPTER EIGHT

Joanna let Steve into her flat, her face grim and stern.

'I've news for you, Steve,' she said as she took his coat and went to pour him a drink. 'And it's not good news, either!'

Steve sighed.

'I'd have been very surprised if it was!' he said bitterly.

For two days, he had worried himself sick about Kerry. She came to work as usual but looked deathly tired. He had tried to send her home but she had politely but firmly refused to go until the rest of the girls left at the usual closing time. He had hoped that she would confide in him—at least give him some idea as to whether Luke was really going to stay permanently at the cottage; whether the marriage was really 'on' again and not just a transient whim of Luke's to get Kerry under his thumb again. But Kerry, though polite and friendly as usual, never mentioned her husband to him or asked him round to coffee or a meal.

Finally he had telephoned Joanna. Kerry's cousin had been as appalled as he had been to hear Luke was down at the cottage. Why? Why? she had asked. When Steve told her he presumed the man was still in love with Kerry after all, Joanna had given him a few rude words in denial.

'Luke isn't capable of loving anyone. There must be some other reason!' she said.

And now she knew the reason and settled down to tell Steve.

'I went round to the flat this morning. It was, of course, empty but I was lucky and found the landlady in. It seems Luke is owing three months' rent—three *months,* Steve! She finally impounded his canvases and anything else of value she could find and locked him out. She told him she was waiting exactly one month for him to pay what he owes and if he doesn't cough up, she'll take him to court.'

Steve shook his head. He was not really surprised—only desperately worried on Kerry's account.

'So Kerry might get dragged into it now he's living with her? Can a wife be made to pay her husband's bills?'

Joanna snorted.

'I didn't take the chance. I paid what was owing. It was worth it to keep Kerry clear of the mess. But I'm not telling Luke I've settled his debts—or at least, not until I hear from Kerry what her plans are for the future. Don't you see, Steve, Luke is making use of her. It isn't *love* that's taken him hotfoot down to Kerry and the cottage; it's to get himself a neat little hide-out.'

'Kerry might not want to believe that, Jo. She told me Luke had changed—that the divorce was off and she was taking him back. It's going to be another shock to hear your news about him.'

'Yes, I know. But I've thought about it all day, Steve, and I'm sure a shock now is better than a further, perhaps bigger disillusionment later. Obviously he'll walk out on her as soon as he makes a bit of money and doesn't need that hide-out any more. What's that going to do to her morale? No, it's better she should know the truth now.'

Steve was silent. What Joanna said made sense and yet he could see nothing but unhappiness for Kerry. She must *love* that man

153

to be able to support, even for a few minutes, his boorish manners and surly behaviour. It sickened him to remember the way Luke had been that night; sickened him to think of Kerry sharing her life with him.

'In a way, this is all my fault!' he said, more to himself than to Jo.

'That's absurd!' Joanna replied quickly. 'What on earth has it got to do with you?'

'I should have asked Kerry to marry me. Don't you see that I failed her when she most needed someone. Maybe if she'd had me behind her, she wouldn't have been taken in by him.'

Joanna leaned across and patted him on the arm with a maternal gesture.

'Put it out of your mind, Steve. You did everything you could for her, short of asking her to marry you. Anyway, she wasn't free to marry you—at least not until the divorce was over. So what difference could it have made?'

'Because I'd have gone to live with her at the cottage. Don't you think I've wanted to live there with her? Every time I've had to go home leaving her there alone, I've been torn in half. I love her, Jo. I wanted to be there to take care of her and watch over her. And I think she might have let me—if I'd been able to accept the child.'

Joanna looked at him compassionately.

'It isn't your fault, Steve. Kerry understood and it was best the way it was. Don't you see that she would have guessed how much you disliked Luke's child even if you'd managed to conceal your feelings from her before it was born. You'd have to be a much better actor than you'll ever be, Steve, to get away with a thing like that. Anyway, it would have been a form of cheating. God knows Kerry has had enough of being cheated by men in her life. It's far better for her to know that she can at least rely on the truth from you.'

Steve scowled.

'I'm no longer sure it is the truth. I'm beginning to think I could put up with the child—for her sake. Now, I suppose, it's too late.'

'Putting up with it isn't loving it, Steve. Kerry would know the difference between loving and tolerating. It just wouldn't work.'

'Oh, hell!' Steve swore softly but emphatically. 'I suppose my feelings are all tied up with jealousy. I want her to have *my* children. Maybe I could have stuck it if I'd not disliked—no, despised, Luke so heartily. I know the baby is half Kerry's but supposing it looked, behaved like its father. Anyway . . .' he added bitterly, 'it's all too late now.'

Joanna stood up.

'I'm going down to see her,' she said. 'Right away this afternoon. If you've got your car you can drive me down. I'm not telling her I'm coming. What I'm hoping to do is to get Luke on his own. And won't I have a thing or two to

155

say to him!'

They drove the thirty odd miles to Sussex in near silence, each lost in their own thoughts. Steve was tormenting himself with the thought that he was in some way to blame for the present situation. Joanna was pondering over how Kerry could ever emerge from the mess into which Luke had dragged her. It was plain enough to Jo, if not to Steve, that Kerry had never stopped loving Luke. Otherwise she could never have been so desperately glad and anxious to bear his child.

Steve drove her to the cottage and switched off the engine. He looked at Jo's plump, capable figure beside him and said:

'Do you want me to come in with you, Joanna?'

She shook her head.

'No, I'll deal with him my way. You're sure Kerry will be at the office?'

'Unless she's unwell, yes! She usually leaves at five-thirty, and gets back here about a quarter to six.'

Joanna glanced at her watch.

'Then that gives me an hour to tell Luke Austin just what I think of him.'

Steve drove off, leaving Joanna to walk up to the cottage and knock on the door. She had to knock three times before Luke, yawning and rubbing his eyes, opened it.

'You? You're Kerry's cousin, Joanna, aren't you? Kerry's not in.'

He stood in the doorway, obviously wakened from sleep, and equally obviously, none too pleased to see her.

'I know! May I come in?'

He looked her up and down and lifted his shoulders.

'I suppose so. There's nothing to drink!' He allowed her to walk past him and kicked the door shut behind them. 'I polished off the remains of your gin the night I arrived. Still, Kerry's promised to bring me back some brandy this evening.'

'Which no doubt she will be paying for!'

'Oh, ho!' Luke said, beginning to enjoy himself. He rather admired Joanna—she was a strong, determined woman able to stand up for herself—do battle. He followed her into the sitting-room and slouched into his usual chair.

'You are broke, I suppose?'

Luke grinned.

'Right first time—not that I see why it is any business of yours.'

Joanna looked him straight in the face.

'Oh, but it is! You see, I happen to know that you are owing your landlady three months' rent. I know, too, that that is the reason you came down here.'

Luke let out his breath. Joanna had shaken him for a moment. But he wasn't all that worried. There was nothing *she* could do to him.

'So what? I still don't see that it is any of

your business!'

'Perhaps not. But it is Kerry's and as soon as she gets home, I intend to tell her.'

This time Luke laughed outright.

'And just what do you think that will do for you? The girl's in love with me. She'll keep me here as long as I want to stay.'

Joanna felt sick and a little frightened. She had not known that Luke was quite so ruthless. She said:

'You forget, Luke, that Kerry is concerned with someone other than you just now. She has her baby to think of and she won't be quite so easily taken in once she knows that you are only making use of her.'

Luke gave Joanna a sudden radiant smile which shocked her. It was so full of charm that for a second, even she was dazzled. Then he said softly:

'D'you know, I rather like you. You and I would get on well together. I see what you're after, of course, but you won't succeed.'

Joanna drew back in her chair, disliking his admiration even more than his erstwhile enmity.

'And why not? I've no doubt you talked Kerry into thinking you were back here because you found you couldn't live without her. Well, Kerry might have been fool enough to believe you—but she won't when she knows the real reason you came.'

Again Luke laughed, quietly, confidently,

almost frighteningly.

'Fat lot you know about her, then. Of course, she won't *like* it—her pride will be hurt. But that won't be the first time. Don't you really understand what it's all about, Joanna? Kerry's *in love* with me. She knows I'm all kinds of a bastard but she doesn't care. She wants me at any price—or should I say, she has made just the one condition—that I accept the baby. Well, I've accepted it. It's no skin off my nose. I shan't have to look after the brat and long before it gets to the tiresome stage where it can't be anchored in a pram, I'll be out of here, I don't doubt. But don't think I'll be fool enough to let Kerry *know* that. She thinks I'm the prodigal husband, returned for good.'

'I'll tell her what you said.'

'You do that thing. Let's see which of us she'd rather believe, you or me? I'm going to enjoy this—might be quite an evening, especially with a bottle of brandy to cheer us all up.

'Luke, you can't! It just isn't fair. You're using her. Haven't you any pity for her at all?'

'I'm not *making* her do anything she doesn't want to do. She wants me. Is that so difficult to understand? Don't you think you might want me some day. Most women seem to find me attractive and I must say, I don't think you're so bad, either. I never realized before quite what a woman you are!'

Joanna stood up as if to strike him. She was the more angry because for a split instant in time, she had seen and recognized this man's physical attraction. When he used that soft, disturbing voice, looked through those half-shut burning dark eyes, a cruel sensual smile on his beautiful mouth, there was a primitive sexuality about him that Joanna could not entirely ignore.

'You disgust me!' she said, letting her hand drop to her side.

He laughed, as if he had been aware of her innermost thoughts and simply did not believe her.

'Well, I don't disgust my wife. And while we're on the subject, let's not forget she is my wife. Do you think you are doing the right thing trying to bust up a happy marriage, Joanna?'

She knew he was trying to annoy her and yet she could not prevent herself rising to the bait.

'You would do well to remember you bust up the marriage,' she said violently.

'And here I am patching it up again. By the way, Beautiful, how come you heard I was here? Kerry didn't tell you, did she? No, well, I suppose it was the boyfriend, then. Put a spike in his guns, didn't I?'

Joanna turned away in disgust. She could not bear to think of her darling Kerry under this man's influence again and yet she was no longer at all sure that she would be able to do anything about it—or, come to that, if she had the right to do anything about it. A marriage was a personal thing—and outsiders had no right to interfere; or at least, not as a rule. But Luke was so evil. It was a strong word and yet she felt it to be true.

She made herself some tea and settled down to wait for Kerry. She did not wait long. At the sound of Kerry's voice in the hall, she jumped to her feet but Luke was there before her, his arm round Kerry in a possessive gesture that turned Joanna cold but which warmed Kerry's heart.

'Your cousin Joanna is here!' Luke was saying as Joanna came into the hall. 'Surprise, surprise!'

Kerry's smile grew deeper. She gave a glad cry and ran to Jo, giving her a childish hug.

'Oh, how lovely, Jo! The two people I love most in the world, both here together.'

Jo's heart sank. Kerry was so obviously happy, so much on top of the world, had she the heart to wipe that smile from her face? She remained silent and followed the other two into the sitting-room.

Luke was being very solicitous. He removed Kerry's coat and helped her into a chair. Then he sat on the edge of it, his arm round Kerry's shoulders. Kerry's face glowed.

'Luke's come to live here, with me!' she said to Jo and then gave a shy smile. 'But I expect he has told you. What time did you arrive, Jo?

161

Are you staying the night? Luke's in the spare room as I'm not sleeping too well and it's less disturbing for him, but we could easily put the camp bed up down here . . .'

Joanna had meant to return to London but now she decided to accept Kerry's offer. For the moment, anyway, she could not bring herself to tell Kerry what she knew about Luke running into debt. Maybe there would be an opportunity tomorrow—if she could get Kerry alone.

But Luke, guessing her thoughts, stayed close to Kerry. He was very attentive, cosseting her, refusing to allow her to lift the logs; even offering to cook the supper for them. In the end, Joanna did the cooking.

While she was out of the room, Luke said to his wife:

'I'm afraid your cousin doesn't like me much. It's a pity as I'm rather taken by her. It would have been nicer all round if we could have been friends!'

Kerry leant back in her chair, her eyes shut, her whole being relaxed and incredibly happy. These last two days had not been quite so perfect. It was wonderful to wake up and know Luke was there, with her in the cottage; that he would still be there when she came home from work. But although he had not been actually unpleasant, he had not gone out of his way to be very pleasant or helpful. He seemed quite happy to have her wait on him, fuss over

162

him, never offering to do any of the chores despite the fact that the birth of the baby was only a month away now and she was becoming very cumbersome and slow. But this evening he was being nicer to her than he had ever been since the brief interlude of their affair—before they were married. He was affectionate, protective, considerate—the perfect husband.

She wondered now at this transformation. Maybe Jo had been having a talk with him. Whatever the cause, she was not going to question it. It was enough that Luke was back and being so charming to her. She smiled up at him, and answering his last remark, said:

'Jo will soon see for herself what a good husband you can be! You've got to remember, Luke, that she is more like an aunt than a cousin—she feels she has to look after me. Naturally she was angry on my account when . . . when our marriage bust up.'

Luke did not argue the point. He couldn't really care less about Jo's opinion of him. He merely wanted to ensure that he stayed here until the pressure was off. What Jo didn't know was that he had a few other creditors; the landlord at the pub where he'd been buying his drink on tick; the delicatessen round the corner from the flat where he hadn't paid his bill to the trusting little Italian who ran it, for nearly six months. No, he was well out of the way—out of sight, out of mind.

'I think your cousin doesn't trust me. Do

you know, Katriona, she actually went to the trouble of spying on me? Went round and saw our landlady at the studio and found out I owed a few weeks' rent. Really, I should hardly have thought it was any of her business.'

The smile left Kerry's face. She was surprised at Jo; and worried, too, despite the light-hearted tone of Luke's voice.

'How much is owing, Luke? Is it a lot? She's not trying to throw you out?'

'Good heavens, no!' Luke said quickly, airily. 'Anyway, if you're willing to put up with me here, I might give up the studio. After all, why run two homes!'

'Oh, Luke!' Her eyes were shining with pleasure, his debts momentarily forgotten. 'Do you mean that? Somehow it makes all the difference to know that you really do mean to make a fresh start with me here. I wouldn't want to go back to the studio—not with a baby; and anyway, it has such unhappy memories. Here it's as if we are beginning our marriage all over again.'

'I'll write to her tomorrow and give her notice!' Luke said, squeezing her hand. 'I suppose I'd better pay her off—not that I'll be able to right this minute—I've been pretty slack about trying to sell my pictures lately, so I'm stony. But I'll get cracking as soon as I can.'

'I can lend you some money, Luke!' Kerry cried eagerly. 'I've saved nearly a hundred pounds since I've been here. It's for the baby but he won't need it for a while so I can easily lend it to you. I'll go to the bank tomorrow.'

Luke protested half-heartedly, but Kerry was adamant.

'You can pay it back as soon as you've sold a picture. You didn't bring any paints with you, Luke. Ought you to go and get them?'

Luke looked down at her with his enigmatic smile.

'I wasn't to know if you'd have me back, Kerry. There wasn't much point carting all my stuff down if you were going to throw me out, was there?'

She was surprised, and delighted, at this new humility. In the old days Luke would have taken it for granted she'd have him back. Luke had changed . . . there was no doubt about it. Jo would see for herself . . .

'Supper's ready!' Jo called from the kitchen. Luke helped Kerry to her feet and stood for a moment with his hands on her shoulders, looking into her face. She had lost that drawn, thin, haggard look. Her face was fuller, her hair shining and glossy. There were shadows of tiredness beneath her eyes but they shone at him with a brilliance that vaguely disturbed him. He said:

'It'll be a good thing when that child is born; then I can get my arms round you properly!'

She felt the faint stirrings of the old desire for him and his words made her even more

165

excited and happy. He still found her attractive—even like this! It would be nice to be slim again; to be able to move quickly and to bend when she wanted. She, too, was impatient now for the child to be born.

Joanna watched them come into the room, arm in arm, and her mouth tightened. Kerry might be taken in by Luke but not she! Luke would use Kerry just for so long as it suited him; then he would drop her without a thought for the mental agony he would put her through. There was only one sort of love Luke knew—self-love.

She looked at Kerry's bright, happy face and felt like crying. She was no longer sure that she could tell Kerry tomorrow that she had paid Luke's debts. It might be kinder after all, to let her have her brief moment of happiness. Luke himself had admitted that it would not last.

CHAPTER NINE

Steve fought hard against the temptation to visit Kerry. She had finally stopped work and would not be back at the office until a month after her baby was born—on doctor's orders; so he no longer saw her daily at the office where he could reassure himself that all was well with her.

He had heard from Joanna that Kerry was

well and happy. Luke, so Joanna said, was playing the model husband and Kerry firmly believed that he was a changed person. But not so changed that he was prepared to put Kerry's wishes before his own. He had said to Jo:

'I'd just as soon you didn't come down again for a while! I know you and Kat are pretty thick but I prefer to have her to myself—if you don't mind!'

If Kerry had wanted her to, Joanna would have visited her again despite Luke. But Kerry seemed to have fallen hopelessly under Luke's spell and was perfectly content to be isolated from the rest of the world now she had Luke back.

'All the same, I don't like it!' Joanna had told Steve. 'I just don't trust him. I can't help wondering how much work he's doing—not just painting, but around the cottage. He was attentive enough when I was there but I'm damned sure it was put on for my benefit. Kerry must be feeling pretty exhausted right now with only a few weeks to go and I'm worried stiff about her. I wish you could drop in on them, Steve.'

He, too, wanted reassurance. But at the same time, he wasn't sure he could stand the sight of Luke Austin. His jealousy was acute and he wasn't sure he could be polite even for Kerry's sake.

Miserably, he remembered the happy times

he and Kerry had had together at the cottage. Did *she* remember? he wondered. Now another man sat in his chair by the fire; ate at his place at the table; read the books from the book shelves he had put up . . .

'I won't go!' he told himself firmly a hundred times a day. 'Damned if I'll go!'

But the following Saturday morning, he got out his car and drove round to the cottage, unable to bear another sleepless night worrying over Kerry. He had to see for himself that she was all right.

In his coat pocket he had some papers she had typed. He had invented a stupid query about the contents as an excuse for going there.

He knocked three times before the door was opened. Kerry stood looking at him with a dawning smile of welcome.

'Why, Steve! What a nice surprise. Come in!'

Although it was after ten-thirty, Luke, apparently, had not yet got up. Apologetically Kerry explained that he had not been sleeping too well and needed the lie-in.

From the state of the sitting-room, it was obvious to Steve that he had walked into the middle of Kerry's efforts to clean up. The grate was half empty and paper and sticks were ready to lay the fire. This was not apparently one of the chores Luke did to assist Kerry.

'Sorry about the mess!' Kerry apologized

168

ruefully. 'I'm afraid it takes me a month of Sundays to do anything now if it involves bending down.'

'Let me help!' Steve offered quickly. 'I'll get the logs and coal in for you, shall I?'

She accepted his offer gratefully and five minutes later, they had the fire going. Kerry sat down in the armchair and drew a deep breath.

'I'll be glad when it's over,' she said quietly. 'I just don't seem to have much energy for anything right now.'

Steve stifled his criticism of Luke. It was none of his business that the lazy devil chose to lie in bed while his wife struggled to manage in her present condition. He hoped for his own sake that Luke would stay in bed and leave him these few minutes in peace with Kerry. But almost at once, Luke put in an appearance. Steve was shocked. The man was in his dressing-gown, unshaven, his hair unbrushed, his face grey beneath a stubble of beard.

'Where's the brandy, Kat?' he asked, nodding at Steve in an off-hand way. 'God, my head! Get the brandy, Kerry, for pity's sake.'

Kerry's face flushed. She got up with an effort but hesitated and said quietly:

'Do you think you should, Luke? You had nearly a whole bottle last night and . . .'

'Get the bloody brandy!'

Steve, shocked and dismayed, stood up.

'I don't think you should speak to Kerry like that. I . . .'

Luke swung round, his face furious.

'You shut up. I don't give a damn what you think. I'll get the blasted bottle myself!'

He lurched across to the table where a bottle, three parts empty, stood beside a dirty glass and and ashtray of stubs. He ignored the glass, clutched the bottle and shambled out of the room. Steve sat down again, tongue-tied by the distress in Kerry's face.

'I . . . he . . . he isn't usually like this!' Her voice was pleading with him to understand. 'It's just that he had some bad news yesterday and he had a bit too much to drink last night.'

Suddenly, to his horror, she burst into tears. He was on his feet at once, his arms round her shoulders.

'Kerry, for God's sake, don't. You don't have to apologize to me. You know that!'

'Oh, Steve!' She sniffed and blew her nose on the handkerchief he offered her and tried to smile. But the tears were beginning to fall again. 'Everything was going so well!' she said. 'Luke was happy here until . . . until he realized he would have to start work again, make some money. I had some saved up which I lent him, but when he went up to London he had a few bills to pay off and . . . suddenly the money was all used up. Luke thought he could sell some paintings but yesterday morning he had a letter from a friend of his who had been trying to sell some pictures for him and he said it was useless. Luke was terribly upset—that's why he got . . . got drunk last night. I know it isn't that he's worried so much for himself—it's because he has spent my money and can't pay me back.'

Steve's mouth tightened. He, better than most people, knew just how hard Kerry had had to work for that money; how determined she had been to have at least a hundred pounds in the bank before the baby was born. She'd reached her target, too. She had celebrated the day with him a week or two before Luke had reappeared on the scene.

What in heaven's name had Luke spent the money on? He must have had some pretty big bills outstanding to have got through that amount in three weeks. He tried to hide his concern from Kerry and said jokingly:

'It's you, not Luke, who ought to have got tight. Now stop worrying, darling.' The endearment was out before he could stop it. 'If you're in difficulties, you know I'll give you a cheque right now. And don't argue about it—there's fifty pounds due to you—Christmas bonus, as it happens.'

Kerry stared at him, wide-eyed.

'But I'm not entitled to a bonus.'

'Indeed you are. Everyone in the office is getting one—we've had a particularly successful year. I didn't mention it before . . .' the lies came easily now that he had started

'. . . as I was saving it up for a Christmas surprise. So there it is. Every cloud has a silver lining.'

He took out his cheque book and wrote in the amount quickly, before she could argue about it or attempt to stop him. As he gave it to her, he said quietly:

'I know it's your money, Kerry, to do with as you please. But this time, I should really keep it in the bank—you might need it for the baby and I'm sure things will improve for Luke. He can always get a job, can't he? I mean, other than painting.'

Kerry nodded. She knew Steve was right—that she ought to have this money behind her. But what Steve did not know was how much higher all the household bills were now that Luke was living here. Food bills had more than doubled; meat, vegetables, milk . . . it had all gone up quite frighteningly . . . and now there was a drink bill as well. Somehow she must explain to Luke that they couldn't afford for him to drink brandy. Until she was working again, he'd have to be content with beer. Even that was really more than she could afford if she was to manage on her savings for the next two months.

Steve was on the point of leaving when Luke reappeared. It was obvious at once to Steve that the man was now quite drunk. He held the empty bottle in his hand and stumbled across the room to Kerry.

'S'empty!' he said. 'Go'n get 'nother one!'

'No Luke! I can't . . . I haven't any money!'

'Then ask the boyfriend to cough up. Sure he owes you something for past favours, eh?' Luke smirked and Kerry's face tightened in dismay. 'G'on, then. I wanna drink, *now!*'

His voice was rising and Steve felt forced to intervene—to protect Kerry from the scene that must inevitably follow if Luke were refused the brandy he wanted.

'Come on back to bed!' he said firmly, taking Luke's arm.

'You mine y'own business!' Luke swore truculently. 'You gonna get my bottle or do I have to make Kat get it? One of you's gonna get it, see?'

Steve knew that he was the stronger of the two—he was taller, heavier than Luke and if it came to a test of strength, he could pick the man up and force him into the bedroom—lock him in if necessary. But he didn't want to make Kerry witness such a scene. She was as white as a ghost and trembling. He put his hands in his pocket and took out two pound notes.

'All right. Here's some money. You go and get it yourself,' he said quietly.

Luke looked at the notes, then at Steve, and lastly at Kerry. The anger died out of his face, but a look of cunning replaced it. 'Can't go out like this . . .' he said, pointing to his dressing-gown and pyjamas. 'Kat'll have to go. You'll go, won't you, my loving lil' wife?'

173

Steve felt sick. He couldn't stand this—not for himself but for Kerry. It appalled him beyond measure that she could love this man; that she should let herself be a party to such a state of affairs.

'I can't go, Luke. I'm not well.'

Luke's face became threatening.

'You bloody well will go. I'm telling you to go, see? Now. "Not well" my foot! Jus' 'cos you're gonna have a baby doesn't mean you can't walk. G'on. Now. I want that drink now.'

'I'll go!' Steve said quickly, but Kerry stood up, her face ashen but determined.

'No, Steve. This isn't your worry—it's mine. I'll go.'

'Damned if you will!' Steve said violently. 'I've got my car outside. I'll drive you, Kerry!' It seemed a brilliant idea—it would get Kerry out of the house—away from Luke. 'Come along, we'll go together.'

'You bloody won't!' Luke's voice was shrill. 'Not getting away with *that*. I know what you'll do to her once you get her out of here, you'll . . .'

Kerry's cry of protest synchronized with Steve's raised arm.

'You say anything like that again and I'll smash your face in!' Steve shouted. Kerry caught his arm, pleading with him.

'Steve, don't, please, don't . .

'You will, will you?' Quietly, deliberately, Luke repeated the sentence. He was not too

174

drunk to know he was invoking a fight. He wanted a fight—anything to relieve the boredom of the last week. He was too drunk to be afraid of anyone.

But Steve was sober—sober enough to know he couldn't hit a drunk man, and he couldn't ignore Kerry's pleas to stop. His arm dropped to his side. But Luke wanted a fight. He lurched across the room, stopping only to pick up a wrought iron lampstand as a weapon.

Kerry screamed. Steve tried to push her out of the way as he saw Luke approaching, but she let go his arm and turned instead towards Luke. It all happened so quickly. He was powerless to stop the heavy blow as it swerved down, caught the side of Kerry's face and then landed with a sickening thud against her side.

She fell at once—not moving but giving one animal-like cry of pain as she crumpled up. Steve dropped to his knees beside her and Luke, suddenly aware of what he had done, stopped like a statue, his arm still holding the lamp-stand, his face fuddled and frightened.

'Get a doctor—at once!' Steve's voice was a sharp command. As Luke still stood there, he got up, pushed him to one side and went to the phone himself. When he finished speaking, he came back and looked into Luke's face.

'If you've killed her, I'll bloody well kill you!' he said.

He was so angry that he wondered in momentary madness, whether he might not kill him anyway. Then Kerry moaned and he forgot Luke as he dropped down to the floor beside her and cradled her head in his arms.

CHAPTER TEN

She was very ill. Now and again she floated out of a nightmare and was conscious of a nurse, of the patterned flowers on the screens round her bed, of thirst. Then the pain would take hold of her and grow and grow until she was back in the nightmare again.

Sometimes Jo was there beside her; sometimes it was Steve. Once it was Luke, looking white and frightened.

'Don't be frightened of me!' she whispered. Then she was suddenly terribly frightened of him—he was part of the nightmares and she began to scream and Luke went away.

She tried hard to stay awake. She knew that if she let herself go, she might fall asleep forever. Her body wanted to sleep forever, but she wanted to live. She had to live so that when her baby was born it would have a mother. For her baby's sake, she must try to stay awake; to fight the tiredness. Being awake meant pain—but she must bear with the pain. Don't sleep, don't sleep! she told herself. Then the nurse would prick her arm and presently she would fall asleep despite her effort of will.

Her moments of consciousness became more frequent. The doctors and nurses watched her closely. The Ward Sister said to Jo:

'It's incredible, really, to see how some people fight for life. She's fighting every inch of the way. Life must be very precious to her to make her want to live so much.'

Joanna bit her lip, trying not to weep. Kerry's life precious! She had lost the one thing in the world she wanted to live for—her baby. It had been stillborn. Sometime soon, Kerry would have to know. Someone would have to break the news to her—break her heart.

Luke had gone. He had paid one visit to the hospital and then he had gone back to London. Joanna, unable to bring herself to speak to him, was unsure how he felt. He looked pretty badly shaken, but then one never knew with Luke how much was pretence, how much genuine. The only words he spoke were:

'You can't blame me—it was an accident!'

Steve had confirmed this, of course. Luke had not struck Kerry deliberately. The blow had been intended for Steve. If Steve had wanted to, he might have been able to prefer charges but he wouldn't do that—for Kerry's sake. Steve was barely coherent when talking of Luke.

'Keep him out of my sight, Jo, or I'll kill him!'

177

He practically lived at the hospital, spending long hours by Kerry's bedside, relinquishing his post only when Jo came to replace him. It was Steve who had insisted on a private room, the best specialist from London to care for her after the emergency operation. But for all his thoughtfulness, it had been too late to save the baby. It wasn't even certain for the first week if Kerry herself would live.

Jo moved into the cottage so that she could be near to the hospital. Steve spent the nights there but Jo knew he didn't sleep. He would pace the floor for hours on end, smoking, tormenting himself, with the thought that but for him, the accident might never have happened.

'Steve, Luke was drunk! If he hadn't had you there to vent his anger on, he'd have turned on Kerry. Sooner or later, he would have hit out at her. He didn't love her. In a way, I think he despised her for loving him the way she did. He thought it weak and stupid. He was just making use of her—the moment he had some money of his own, he'd have gone anyway.'

She hid from him her own deep fear for Kerry's life. Luke's blow had killed the baby and injured Kerry internally. Kerry was fighting to live. But Joanna realized that she would give up the fight the moment she became aware of the fact that her baby was dead.

It was a week before Kerry was conscious for long enough to ask what had happened. Steve was there, and the nurse.

The nurse, following her orders, said:

'You've had an accident, my dear, but you're going to be all right.'

'And . . . my . . . baby?'

'Everything is all right!' said the nurse firmly. 'Look, there's a friend of yours here— waiting to talk to you!'

Kerry's eyes turned to where Steve sat. 'Steve!' she whispered. 'I'm glad you're here!'

'I love you, Kerry. I love you!' He did not care that the nurse should hear him. It mattered only that Kerry should know.

'I know you do, Steve,' she said softly, and before he could say any more, she was again asleep.

Steve turned to the nurse, his face anguished. 'She isn't dying, is she? Sister said she was better. Why does she sleep so much?'

'She's under sedation,' the nurse explained. 'She has to be heavily drugged because of the pain. She isn't going to die—she's just sleeping.'

Steve continued his patient vigil by her bed. But fortunately for him, it was Jo who happened to be there when Kerry first realized she had lost her baby.

'It's dead, isn't it?' she said flatly, her eyes looking so directly into Jo's that the older woman was unable to voice the denial she had

179

been about to give. There were no tears in Kerry's eyes, only pain and resignation.

'What was my baby—a boy?'

Jo nodded, her own eyes filling with tears. Life seemed so desperately unfair—Kerry had suffered so much. Now this, too.

Kerry's voice, barely audible, said bitterly: 'Steve will be glad!'

Jo was jolted out of her silence.

'Oh, no, Kerry—he's desperately upset—for your sake. I don't suppose you realize it but he has practically lived here at your bedside ever since . . . ever since the accident. He has been quite frantic with worry about you. He loves you very much, Kerry—enough that he would give you back your baby if he could.'

Kerry showed no sign of emotion. Her voice was flat—matter of fact.

'I suppose Luke has gone?'

Jo nodded, surprised and immensely relieved that Kerry did not seem to be taking Luke's absence too much to heart. Maybe the loss of her baby overshadowed any other pain.

'You tried to warn me so often about Luke, didn't you, Jo!'

It was a statement of fact rather than a question.

'I never wanted to listen although right deep down inside, I suppose I knew you were right about him. He was no good—no good at all. Yet I loved him. I hoped so much when he came down to the cottage, he really had changed; that we would be able to settle down to a real married life together.'

'Oh, Kerry, how could you have believed that possible with Luke?'

Kerry grimaced.

'I don't mean the conventional type of married bliss. I know it never could be like that with Luke. He was too self-centred, too egotistical ever to be the loving husband and father. But I wouldn't have minded that—not if underneath he had really loved me.'

'Luke was never capable of loving anyone but himself. You know the real reason he came down to the cottage?'

Kerry nodded.

'He was broke, wasn't he? He borrowed a lot of money from me to pay off his debts. I don't mind about the money—only that Luke should have let me hope again. I would have respected him more if he had come to me openly with the truth—that he needed help. I would have helped him, too—just the same. He should have known that.'

'Then it's all over for good this time?'

Again Kerry nodded.

'Everything is finished, Jo. I don't care what happens to me now. I just don't care any more.'

Jo caught her hand and held it tightly.

'You've got to care, Kerry. You're still young—you've years ahead of you to be happy.'

There was no answering response in Kerry's face. Jo said quietly:

'You'll feel quite differently as soon as you are well again. You've been pretty ill, Kerry, and it is bound to leave you feeling weak and depressed. Just wait a few weeks. You'll see, darling, life will begin to mean something to you.'

Kerry's mouth twisted painfully.

'I wish they had let me die!' she said quietly. 'I just wish you had all let me die!'

Kerry's mental depression did not seem to improve as the days went by. Jo and Steve spent hours discussing what they could do to bring her back to life as well as health. Physically, she was getting stronger. Finally Steve said:

'I'll take her away, Jo—right away somewhere abroad. I know she won't consider marrying me or anything like that yet, but if we could be as we were that wonderful week in Italy—maybe then she would let me love her and look after her.'

At first Kerry refused to agree to Steve's plan. She argued with Jo about it, showing the first faint signs of being sufficiently emotionally aroused to care one way or another.

'I'm not in love with him—I can't marry him—ever. It wouldn't be fair to go feeling as I do.'

'Kerry, he wants to take you—*no strings*

attached. He just wants to give you a good holiday. He knows you don't care—but he wants a chance to make you care. Is that so unreasonable? If it doesn't work, then neither of you are any the worse off than you are now. You wouldn't be making any promises. Steve understands. Go with him, Kerry—if not to please yourself, then to please me.'

Finally, Kerry gave way. But she took no interest in the coloured brochures Steve brought round to the cottage where she was now convalescing in Jo's care. She was polite, even grateful for his plans for her, but never showed the faintest sign of excitement and it was obvious to both her companions that her interest was forced.

In the end Steve had to make the decision where to go, himself. Since Kerry showed no sentimental preference for Italy, he decided against returning to Florence. He chose an incredibly romantic-looking hotel built on to a rocky promentary in the South of France. *Les Roches Fleuries* looked down from the flower-covered rocks into the blue Mediterranean and promised the height of comfort with the most beautiful surroundings anyone could wish for. Here, surely, even Kerry would not be able to resist the call back to life.

They flew to Nice in a Comet. Jo was at London Airport to see them off. She felt more than a little anxious as the great plane soared off the ground into the air. Steve had been so

183

full of hope—Kerry so devoid of it. Could these two weeks in entirely new and lovely surroundings break through that terrible indifference with which Kerry had faced life ever since she realized she had lost her child? In Kerry's shoes, Jo could not have resisted Steve. Yet she could understand her young cousin's invulnerability. She had been wounded too deeply for lesser emotions to touch her now.

Steve, too, was anxious. Kerry did not try to withdraw her hand from his as he sat beside her in the plane, but there was no shadow of response within her hand. He was just a person to her—not a man who loved her beyond count. She was quite indifferent to him except as a friend.

He had hired a car to drive from Nice Airport to Le Lavendou, the seaside village about ninety kilometres from Nice where *Les Roches Fleuries* was situated. Kerry sat beside him, turning her head to watch as he pointed out the beautiful coast line; the romantic white yachts anchored in Cannes harbour; the extraordinary loud noise of the crickets in the fir trees that grew down to the sandy beaches tucked among the rocks. She saw and admired but was not stirred, as he was.

Even the hot sun on her face seemed powerless to bring any warmth into her heart.

That night, they dined on the terrace which was built so far out onto the rocks that looking down, one could believe one was on a liner far out to sea. To heighten the illusion, ships' lanterns were strung along the protecting rail. A canvas awning had been drawn back so that the sky, brilliant with stars, hung seemingly just above their heads. A floodlight from the hotel shone on the dark water and a late, lone swimmer was churning the water into a fish-like foam as he paddled out to the raft in the passage of white light. Beyond, little boats sped past, their lights twinkling from the masts like stars, reflecting in the water.

Steve sighed, stirred deeply by so much beauty. Across the table Kerry sat like a statue, beautiful but remote. He did not dare to ask if she was happy for he knew the answer. She was neither happy nor sad.

She was wearing a new dress—a simple black sheath with tiny straps over her pale shoulders. She had lost that round fullness of face she had acquired during pregnancy and now her cheekbones stood out sharply in the oval whiteness of her profile. Because of this, her eyes seemed larger than ever—great silent pools of mystery.

Beyond even his loving compassion for her, was his desire for her. Unlike that time in Italy, when she had been anxious for his love, he was now forced to disguise his passionate longing for her. He had booked single rooms for them, knowing that this time, he must give no indication of his need for her until she came to him. And she had never seemed so far away—so lost to him.

After dinner, he took her for a walk along the dusty road to Aiguebelle Plage. Tomorrow, he told her, they would come here to this sandy beach and lie in the sun and swim in the water which the barman had told him was nearly 80 degrees.

'For two whole weeks we shall be able to be utterly lazy!' he said softly. 'You shall do just whatever you want, Kerry. You just have to say.'

She returned the pressure of his hand and for a moment, he hoped that the magic of the place was beginning to touch her. It was all so beautiful—a place made for lovers, for honeymooners, for people who wanted to share this beauty with each other. But then she shivered and drawing the cyclamen wool stole closer round her shoulders, said:

'I'm tired, Steve. I think I'd like to go back to the hotel.'

He kissed her outside the door of her room—a gentle kiss on her forehead which was nevertheless a question. If Kerry understood, she made no sign. She thanked him briefly for bringing her to such a lovely hotel and slipping out of his embrace, went quickly into the privacy of her own room.

Steve, knowing he could not sleep, went back down to the bar. Standing on the little balcony outside her room, Kerry watched him

186

walk across the road and down the steps which led to the public rooms of the hotel. Her eyes were full of tears. Strangely, she had not been able to cry for herself—not one tear during those weeks she had lain in hospital. And now, still, she could not cry for herself. It was for Steve she wept; for dear, kind, faithful Steve who could still hope when there was no hope left. She ought not to have come. Jo had failed to understand that there could be no future for her or for Steve because no matter how empty life might be without him, she could never love him. She could never love anyone, ever again.

Below her balcony, the waves beat softly against the rocks. To some, the sound might have been soothing—like a lullaby. But to Kerry they were remorseless, persistent, tragic reminders that nature too, was remorseless, unalterable and unremittingly cruel.

CHAPTER ELEVEN

Steve was desperate. They had been at the hotel for a week now and although Kerry was showing signs of physical recovery, her mental apathy was unchanged. Her body had grown brown with the sun and salt of the sea; her figure filled out a little with all the rich, tempting food. Sleep had erased the shadows from beneath her eyes but not the shadows in them.

He was beginning to lose hope. As he lay beside her in the hot sun, his face turned towards her, he could see nothing of her expression behind the sunglasses. She looked warm, relaxed and very, very desirable in her ice blue bikini. He longed with a longing that was like a sickness, to put out his hand and touch that golden brown body, and feel some response. But Kerry was, by her complete indifference, untouchable. He meant nothing to her as a man—only as a friend. It was incomprehensible to him that she could not be aware of the intensity of his love for her. It was so acute that he could not hide it, nor even tried to do so. Nor was there need, for Kerry was so shut off in her mind that he was quite outside her own circle of feeling.

Would it ever be any different? When he had first arrived here, he had been so sure that the romantic setting and relaxed holiday atmosphere would have their effect on her and that the sun would kiss her back to life as the Prince had kissed the Sleeping Beauty awake. But still Kerry slept, encased in her apparent indifference to any feeling. The sun had kissed her body but had left her heart still frozen.

She stirred, lifting a hand and letting the golden grains of sand run out through her fingers. He said quickly:

'Happy, darling?'

'Of course. It's lovely here, Steve. I'm

feeling so much better.'

'And looking it!' Steve added fervently. 'You're not bored, Kerry?'

There was little to do here other than to lie in the sun, bathe in the translucent warm water, eat and sleep. At night they sat on the terrace talking, about Jo or his work or the cottage. But never about Luke or the baby; never about the future . . .

Again the thought crossed his mind, not without bitterness, that this was a place for honeymooners, for lovers. It was tantalizing to be in such surroundings, so close to Kerry and yet never so far away from her.

He reached out and imprisoned her hand. Her fingers neither returned the pressure of his, nor drew away. He felt he could not bear it. He said suddenly with a hoarse urgency in his voice:

'Kerry, will you marry me?'

He was watching her face closely and saw the pulse in her throat, the grip of her small white teeth over her lower lip. At last, at last, he had touched in her some response.

'Steve, I wish you hadn't asked me. I can't. You know I can't.'

'But, Kerry . . .'

'Must we talk about it? Can't we go on as we are?'

Steve let her hand fall. He said bitterly:

'Just good friends? I don't think I can, Kerry. I love you so much. And I have loved

189

you for so long. You say you can't marry me . . . won't you at least give me a reason?'

She was silent, motionless. He waited a moment or two for her to speak and then said quietly:

'I know you don't love me. I am not asking you to love me—only that you should give me the right to stay with you always; to look after you, to give you my love.'

'Steve, you know it wouldn't work. You'd want more . . . more than I could give you; more than I can ever give anyone.'

He looked so desperate, so unhappy that pity nearly compelled her to weaken. Until this moment, all her pity had been for herself. Now Steve had made her uncomfortably aware of the fact that he was as unhappy as she. The thought hurt—for she was deeply fond of and grateful to Steve and would not have chosen to be the means of hurting the one person in the world who had tried so hard to make her happy. He had tried so hard—and it was no good. It never had been any good. She remembered Italy and the week they had shared there, when for a brief while she had let herself believe she loved him and could be happy without Luke. But it hadn't lasted. Steve's love had been, and still was, a balm to her aching wounds but that was all. She could take from him but had nothing to give him. She felt only half a person now. The old Kerry who had lived on hope of a miraculously changed Luke, was gone for ever. That childish faith in the ultimate goodness of life was gone. Her baby was gone and she could not believe a time would ever come when she would be able to think of her lost child without a tearing, aching loneliness.

Steve and Jo were the two people who kept her sane. She knew that and knew what she owed to them both. But marriage with Steve was no longer thinkable. For a marriage to succeed, and no one knew this better than Kerry, love had to be two-sided.

'I'm so sorry!' she said, feeling the inadequacy of the words. 'I'm afraid I've never been anything but a handicap to you, Steve. You should have been married years ago—to someone else.'

'If it cannot be to you, then I shall never marry!' Steve said with an effort. His disappointment was so acute that words were a difficulty. He had not really hoped for more with his mind, but his heart had cried out with the faintest possibility . . .

'Come!' he said quietly. 'It must be nearly lunchtime. Let's have a quick swim first.'

That evening, when Kerry had retired to her room, Steve stayed on the terrace in the warm night air, writing to Jo.

'You will be very happy with Kerry's physical recovery,' he wrote.

'She is brown and has lost that tense

desperate look and is at last eating well. However, I am unable to advise you as to her state of mind, because she remains shut up inside herself and I know nothing of her feelings—except that she has none for me.

This morning I asked her to marry me. I did not expect her love—only that she should allow me to take care of her from now on. But as you could probably have warned me, she turned me down. I think for a moment she was tempted to say yes— not because she loves me but because she does so badly need someone to give her life direction and meaning. But she is far too honest and genuine a person to marry me just because she needs me and as she has no love for me, there is little hope for the future.

For the rest of our holiday, I shall try not to think of tomorrow. To do so would be unbearable, as I have decided once we get back to England, not to go on seeing Kerry. I don't think I could trust myself to be "just a friend" . . . I want so much more. I shall probably move out of the district and start an agency elsewhere—somewhere far from the temptation of Kerry's presence. I shall have to rely on you, Joanna, to take care of her and you know that any kind of help I can provide anonymously, will always be there. I intend to place a sum of money to your credit at the bank, for you to draw on for Kerry should she ever need it. You must not refuse this or I could never make the clean break that I think is all that is left and best to do.

I trust you will not feel that I am deserting Kerry at the wrong time. I have a feeling that the time has passed when she has need of me and that from now on, if I stayed in her life, I would merely be an additional problem for her.

Please do me a favour and get Interflora to send some flowers to the cottage to welcome Kerry home. Perhaps you, too, could manage to get down that Saturday as I intend to say good-bye to her at the Airport. I may even cancel my flight home and go on somewhere from Nice—I don't know yet. But if you will be able to meet her at London Airport, then I should feel free to let her travel home on her own. An airmail letter should reach me if you reply by return.

Yours,

Steve.'

Four days later, he received Jo's reply.

'My dearest Steve,

Your letter made me happy and deeply unhappy in the next breath. I am so glad Kerry is physically better—that at least is

193

good news. But as for the rest . . . Maybe we were both wrong to hope for anything more from this holiday. It is not so long really, since she was broken in two. Heartbreak is probably the most difficult illness of all to recover from.

Your decision to remove yourself from Kerry's life is, of course, your affair and I will not comment except to say that it would be all wrong for you to have to buy a business elsewhere when you have a perfectly good one where you are. I shall persuade Kerry to give up the cottage and come back to London to the flat with me. She cannot live there alone in any event—it would be far too depressing for her. It was only ever possible because you were on hand. I am writing to invite her to stay with me by the same post and you must do your best to persuade her that this is the best for her. I think she will agree.

Of course I will meet her at London Airport. Wherever you go, Steve, I hope and pray you will find the happiness you deserve. You have been, without doubt, the finest and most wonderful of friends and Kerry is going to miss you far more than you realize.

My love and best wishes and write when you can.

Jo.
P.S. I have organized the flowers.'

Kerry showed him her letter from Jo.

'She wants me to stay in the flat with her,' she told him.

'And?'

She looked at him apathetically.

'I don't know. I suppose I could. Do you think it is a good idea?'

Steve nodded.

'Yes, I do. I think you should write and accept the invitation.'

Kerry sat down and drew out a cigarette which Steve lighted for her.

'It would mean giving up the tenancy of the cottage.'

'I can find another tenant—or I might sell it.'

'I wouldn't be able to see you so often, Steve, though I suppose you would come and visit us in town?'

He couldn't lie to her but he did not want to tell her just yet that he wouldn't be seeing her again after tomorrow—their last day together. He had to keep it to himself or he feared he might break his resolve and be weak, seeking once more to claim from her that which she could not give him. The imminence of that parting was so poignant that he dared not trust himself to speak of it.

'Let's go down to Le Lavendou,' he said. 'I'd like to buy a present for Jo.'

Kerry, too, wanted to go to the village.

Before they went home to England, she wished to buy Steve, as well as Jo, a present. She had never given Steve anything and now, for no particular reason, she wanted to give him a memento of their holiday together.

She walked round the little coastal town unable to make up her mind. Eventually she slipped away from Steve long enough to find her way back to a little side-street where she had noticed some paintings by local artists. Here she found a beautiful pencil sketch of their hotel. It was expensive—drawn, she was told, by an exceptionally clever artist who lived out here.

Kerry paid the fifteen pounds without trying to push the price down. She knew it was an extravagance—that her savings had dwindled to next to nothing and that as soon as she got back to England, she must start work in earnest. But she wanted Steve to have something nice—something he would be able to keep as a reminder of their holiday and her gratitude to him.

He had been very quiet these last few days. She guessed that it was to do with her and supposed her rejection of his proposal was the cause. She tried to give him all the affection she had left in her to give anyone. It wasn't much, but at least she volunteered their goodnight kiss; was the first now to hold his hand where before he would have first sought hers. She could not know that these actions were only making the parting harder for him.

When she gave him the picture later that night, he nearly broke down. It was half a century since he had cried but now there were tears in his eyes. Innocently, Kerry put her arms round his neck and hugged him and said:

'I am going to miss you, Steve!'

And God in heaven, he thought, how I am going to miss you, my beautiful, desirable Kerry. Why haven't I the power to touch you back to life! Why did you have to love a man like Luke Austin? Aren't I at least a better man than he?

But he could say none of these things—only hold her tight in his arms and struggle with the terrible desire to imprison her there forever and to weep as if his own heart were as broken as hers.

Kerry stayed immobile in his embrace, strangely uneasy at his silence; instinct warning her that all was not quite so simple as she had believed.

CHAPTER TWELVE

Jo heard Kerry's key in the front door. There was silence while she hung up her coat and then the door of the little sitting-room opened and Kerry came in. Her hair was windblown, her cheeks whipped to a bright pink by the cold March air.

She dropped on her knees in front of the electric fire and said:

'What wouldn't I give for a bit of Mediterranean sun. It's frantically cold out, Jo!'

Jo poured her a glass of sherry and watched her young cousin as she sipped the amber liquid gratefully. Kerry was quite unaware of the picture she made. She looked about seventeen, rosy-cheeked, carefree, a little tired perhaps, like any other young secretary home from a busy day at the office, but nevertheless young and alive. In three months, the years had rolled away from Kerry. She appeared now exactly as Jo remembered her before her marriage to Luke.

'Chicken curry for supper!' Jo said.

Kerry sniffed the air and wrinkled her nose, grinning.

'Mmm! I can smell it. I'm starving. By the way, Jo, no mail for me today?'

Jo shook her head. Kerry asked the same question every day now when she came home.

And each time she would try to appear casual, unconcerned. Jo hid a smile. She knew that Kerry was wondering why Steve had not written to her since Christmas. He had sent a card and a magnificent crocodile handbag for Kerry, which she had received rapturously. It was the first time she had heard from him since they had been to France on holiday together.

It was not until then that Jo had realized Steve's sudden departure from Kerry's life had affected her young cousin in any way at all. Kerry had been radiant.

'Look, Jo! Isn't it marvellous! Just what I wanted, too. Dear Steve! I wonder how he is . . . what he's doing these days. You'd have thought he would have written to us, wouldn't you? I expect he just wanted time to sort himself out. I'll write to him tonight and give him all our news. Maybe he'll come up to lunch one day next week. You wouldn't mind if I invited him?'

But Steve had not come to lunch—nor answered Kerry's letter. At first, Kerry had come home from work asking, frankly eager:

'Any letter from Steve, Jo?'

But as the weeks went by, she had ceased to mention Steve's name and now, outwardly indifferent, she asked: 'Any mail?'

It was wonderful to know that Kerry was back to normal again; not just back to being the pale, nervous Kerry who had lived with Luke, but the carefree, vital, warm, childish Kerry of her teens.

She finished her glass of sherry and leant back against Jo's knees and said suddenly:

'You know, I do think it's a bit thick. Steve could have answered my letter. I mean, he can't be on holiday or anything—not all this time.'

'Maybe he just doesn't want to see you again, Kerry. You must admit the association wasn't a very happy one for him.'

Kerry tossed her head crossly.

'Oh, don't be silly, Jo. That's all over and done with. I don't mean to re-open that affair—just that it would be nice to be friends. It seems so silly *never* to see each other just because Steve *used* to be in love with me.'

'Maybe he is still in love with you!'

Jo saw the colour flare into Kerry's cheeks.

'That's funny, I must say! If Steve were still in love with me, he would have answered my letter, come to see me. He's probably engaged to someone else or married, for all I know . . . or for all I care. Let's have supper, Jo. Maybe afterwards we could go to the cinema or something.'

Jo let the conversation drop. It was perfectly clear to her that Kerry was piqued by Steve's apparent disinterest in her. But pique was not enough. If Steve knew, he would probably catch the next train to London and Jo didn't want that. He had always been hopelessly weak where Kerry was concerned, with the result that she had taken his love for granted. It was doing her the world of good to be without Steve, ever faithful in the background. But unfortunately, to be piqued was not to be in love and Jo still nursed a secret hope that Kerry and Steve might one day marry.

Luke had disappeared out of Kerry's life

completely. Divorce proceedings had been reopened but this time by Kerry at Jo's suggestion. It had been a simple matter to discover that Luke was living with a new girlfriend at the studio and Kerry's divorce would go through, her solicitor said, without any hitches. Kerry appeared unmoved by the thought that her marriage would soon be dissolved and spoke of it only once to her cousin, telling Jo that she would never, never be able to forgive Luke whom she blamed for the loss of her baby.

But for Jo, Kerry would not have bothered to divorce Luke.

'What's the point, when I shall never marry again!' she had said bitterly. But she had allowed Jo to take the initiative and put an end to a period of her life she wanted to forget for ever.

Kerry had obtained a well-paid job as secretary to a woman who ran a chain of hat shops. She quite enjoyed the work but missed the free and easy atmosphere of Steve's office—or so she told Jo. Jo was not so sure that it wasn't Steve himself Kerry missed but she never mentioned him until his present came at Christmas.

Jo wrote to Steve regularly. He acknowledged her letters with a phone call while Kerry was at work, but he never gave any news of himself. Jo would have stopped the bulletins once Kerry was perfectly fit again if

Steve had not insisted that she write at least every other week.

'Just to let me know she is all right,' he said.

Steve, himself, was not sure why he needed this contact with Kerry through her cousin. He did not question his motives but at the end of every phone call, he always reiterated:

'Be sure and write me next week, Jo!'

In a way, it was stupid of him, he thought, to ask for news of a woman who could no longer have any part in his life. He was not playing the game quite fairly with Diana. Diana was the girl he had made up his mind to marry. She was very young—only just eighteen and she adored him. He knew that each time he took her out, she was hoping he would propose to her. Her youth made it impossible for her to hide from him her hero-worship. The difficulty lay in trying to decide whether this was adolescent hero-worship or the love she believed it to be. As for himself, he was very fond of her. She had a petite, vivacious charm that was hard to resist, more particularly when his self-confidence had been so undermined by Kerry's lack of interest in him as a man. Diana, with her youthful adoration, restored his belief in himself, his ego, his vanity.

But Steve realized all too well that there were several important doubts about such a marriage. First, of course, was that he could never offer any woman but Kerry his whole, unquestioned, undemanding love. He had

202

always sworn that if he could not marry her, he would never marry. What he had really meant was that he could never fall in love again and that remained all too true. He was fond of Diana, deeply fond, and attracted by her, too. There were many men—boys really, who were falling over themselves to date Diana. It was all the more flattering to him that she should prefer him—especially as he had always considered himself rather dull! He wished he could bring himself to feel that it would be right to marry a girl whom you could love, after a fashion, but with whom you could never be in love.

Diana's parents, an important local builder and his wife, liked and approved of him. They made Steve very welcome in their home and by allusion, Steve had gathered that they would consider a marriage with favour; Steve was more than able to support their only child and give her the financial advantages they themselves had always showered on her. But was this approval, Diana's adoration and his own fondness of her enough on which to found a marriage? Steve was still not convinced. He wanted to marry—to settle down, raise a family; wanted to put an end to what seemed like a life-time of loneliness, broken only by those brief days and weeks shared with Kerry. He wanted to be able to forget Kerry completely and yet he could not bring himself to make the break of his own choosing so final that all communication with Joanna should stop, too.

He had not much time left to decide what he should do. Diana's parents were obviously expecting him to declare his intentions, not to mention Diana herself. He could not go on taking her out two or three times a week and continue to parry her half veiled questions as to his feelings for her indefinitely. If only he knew himself! It was possible that marriage might help him finally to forget Kerry. But it was also possible that he would spend his honeymoon wishing it were Kerry and not Diana by his side.

It finally occurred to him that he was at a cross roads in his life and that somehow, he must discover which road he wished to take— that of companionship and a measure of fulfilment, or that of solitary bachelorhood, comforted by his memories and his freedom. The freedom seemed to be holding less and less meaning as the months slipped by.

On a sudden impulse, he wrote to Joanna, asking her advice. Her reply which came by return of post, was brief but sensible.

'Why not come up to town and see Kerry again. You would then know just how much she still means to you. Perhaps you will be able to look into her eyes, touch her hand, see her smile and remain unmoved. That will surely decide for you, that you can

safely many your Diana. On the other hand, you may find yourself still in love with Kerry and then you will know that you haven't the right to marry this girl.'

'Yes!' thought Steve. 'Joanna is right, as always. It may be the hard way but it is certainly a logical one and I owe it to Diana.'

He telephoned Joanna and arranged to go up to London on the following Saturday morning.

'Fine!' said Jo pleasantly. 'We've nothing arranged and we'll both be here. I'll tell Kerry—it'll be a nice surprise for her to see her old friend.'

'Steve's dropping in to see us tomorrow!' she told Kerry on the Friday night. She watched Kerry's eyes widen in surprise and then narrow suddenly when Jo passed on the news that Steve was practically engaged to be married.

'I don't see how you can be "practically" engaged!' Kerry said, her voice uneven, hurried. She turned her back on Jo and said over her shoulder: 'Either he is or he isn't!'

Jo smiled.

'Well, perhaps I should have said that he is about to become engaged. I believe it's to quite a young girl called Diana something or other.'

'And how do you know all this?' Kerry's voice was tight.

'Well, Steve phoned a day or two ago. I forgot to tell you.'

Kerry swung round, her cheeks now bright red.

'Well, you shouldn't have forgotten. After all, Steve's my friend, not yours and . . .' she broke off as she caught Jo's eye.

'We'd better get some beer in. Steve likes a light ale, doesn't he? I think we've only sherry and gin in the cupboard.'

'I don't think I'll be here to entertain him!' Kerry retorted. 'I may be out.'

Jo said softly:

'Don't be childish, Kerry. Of course, you aren't going out and even if you were, you'd have to put it off. As you just said yourself, Steve is your friend, not mine, and what is more, a friend to whom you owe a lot. Whether you want to see him or not, you're going to be here.'

'I'm not a child to be told what to do by you!'

'Then stop behaving like a child.'

It was the nearest to a quarrel they had ever been. Jo was not really angry, for she suspected the cause of Kerry's behaviour, but Kerry herself was miserable. A deep inexplicable depression settled over her. She tried to lose herself in the TV play but the laughter and jokes in the comedy only seemed to deepen her depression. She knew that she ought to be glad. How often in the past had she told Steve he ought to get married, settle down! Now Steve was going to do just that and she was still not satisfied.

'I suppose I'm being selfish!' she told herself silently.

But the truth was, she was hurt. It was not so long since Steve had said: *'If you won't marry me, I'll never marry!'*. And now he was in love with someone else. She slept little that night. She dreamed intermittently of Steve and woke even further confused because in her dreams, she was begging him not to marry anyone else. She blushed in the darkness, ashamed of the subconscious self weeping and holding out her arms to a man who obviously no longer loved her. Angrily, she told herself that when he arrived, she would be particularly cold and remote, indifferent to his plans for his future.

But it wasn't possible to be indifferent. As the morning wore on, she became more and more keyed up and nervous. If she could have escaped from the meeting altogether, she would have done so, but she was all too aware of Jo's eyes watching her; the last thing she wanted was for her cousin to know she cared one iota about Steve. She held her head high, met Jo's gaze casually and underneath was trembling and strung taut with nerves.

At the last minute, when the door bell rang, her nerve went. She all but ran into the kitchen and left Jo to open the door.

In the hallway, she heard Steve's voice greeting her cousin.

'And Kerry? Isn't she here?'

Her hands went to her cheeks as if to push back the rush of colour. She poured herself a glass of Jo's cooking sherry and drank it quickly, feeling slightly sick and no less nervous when she had done so. Then Jo came in, smiling slightly, and said:

'What on earth are you doing in here, Kerry?'

She took Kerry's arm and there was no alternative but to follow her into the sitting room where Steve was sitting in Jo's armchair.

He got to his feet at once and smiled at Kerry. She gave him a quick tremulous smile in return.

'Hullo, Kerry! You're looking wonderfully well. How nice to see you.'

She turned away quickly, busying herself with the cigarette box, wretchedly conscious of the fact that her hands were trembling as she held the box out to him. To cover her confusion, she said hurriedly:

'Jo tells me you're engaged to be married. Do tell us about her, Steve!'

There was a moment of silence and then Steve said quietly:

'I'm not actually engaged—just thinking about it. Jo must have got it wrong.'

'I think it's a wonderful idea!' Kerry heard her own voice, high pitched and unnatural.

She tried to lower the tone. 'It's high time you settled down, Steve. What's she like? Anyone we know?'

He began to tell her about Diana but suddenly there seemed very little to say about the girl he half thought he loved. Now, face to face with Kerry again, he knew that the younger girl meant nothing at all to him. He didn't love her . . . could never love her. His heart belonged irrevocably to this lovely girl, standing so cool and remote listening to him.

Obviously the months apart had been good for her . . . she looked so marvellously well and there was a bright colour in her cheeks that he hadn't seen there for years. Separation from him had done her good! It was a bitter reflection.

Jo broke in on the conversation to tell him that they had prepared lunch for him . . . he must stay. He felt too dejected and miserable to welcome the idea, but he could think of no quick excuse. He wanted to hurry away from the bitter-sweet torment of Kerry's presence and yet another part of him wanted to stay beside her, hearing her voice, seeing her smile.

'I'll go and check on the casserole!' Jo said and suddenly he was alone with Kerry. He could find nothing to say . . . nothing that she would want to hear. The silence between them became heavy and intolerable. Then Kerry said: 'Steve!' just as he began to talk about his work. They stopped and began again simultaneously and broke off suddenly laughing. The tension was gone and they were at ease. Steve said:

'Oh, Kerry, you don't know how I've missed seeing you!'

She stared at him uncertainly, her heart pounding.

'Have you? I would have thought you'd have been too busy—with Diana!'

Steve grinned.

'But there has still been plenty of time to miss you. I suppose you've been busy, too?'

It was a moment or two before she replied. Then she said softly:

'You never answered my letter at Christmas.'

Steve looked surprised.

'I didn't think you particularly wanted to hear from me. And that isn't the only reason I didn't write . . . I thought it might be best . . .'

'Best?'

'Yes! I was trying to remake my life, Kerry— a life without you. So long as I was seeing you, in touch with you by letter, it was impossible to forget you.'

'I see! And since you have come to see me, I take it that you've been able to put the past in the past.'

'I'll *never* stop loving you!'

The words were out before he could stop them. They brought the bright colour flaring back into Kerry's cheeks. They were so

210

sudden, so unexpected, just as the incredible joy in her heart was unexpected.

'That's why I came!' Steve went on honestly. 'I wasn't sure if I ought to marry this girl, feeling as I did about you. I wanted to get married, to settle down, perhaps have children, but at the back of my mind, I knew that it wouldn't be fair to Diana if I couldn't really love her. In fact, it was Jo's idea that I should come here today—to find out once and for all what you meant to me.'

'Oh, Steve!' her voice was husky, deeply moved. She held out her hand and Steve grasped it and gripped it tightly in his own.

'Don't be sorry for me!' he said. 'I'm not unhappy about it. In a way, I'm glad. I don't think the marriage could have worked—it was only an escape from . . . well, from a kind of loneliness. I know now that I can never escape from that kind of loneliness. There is no one else but you in the world who could dispel it.'

'Then you don't love her . . . at all?'

He looked down at her where she now knelt at his feet, both her hands in his, staring up at his face.

'No, not at all. There is no mistaking love when you feel the real thing, is there, Kerry? I suppose this is the way you felt about Luke!'

She shook her head, her eyes suddenly filled with tears.

'No, no, it wasn't that way. Mine was a selfish demanding love. I wanted Luke to be

211

different, the way I wanted him and not the way he was. To love . . . as you love . . . that is a far finer, bigger thing, Steve. I used to think what I felt for Luke *was* love. I lived in torment when I was with him, buoyed up with dreams that Luke could one day be the kind of man I wanted. It's only very recently I've realized what real love is.,

She felt Steve's hands trembling in hers as he said:

'Then you, too, have met someone else?'

She smiled up at him, her eyes bright with tears.

'Yes! I love him very much. It's far more real than the love I had for Luke. It's a feeling of rightness, of belonging, of wanting to give and to serve and be near to him always . . .'

With an effort, Steve said:

'And do I know him?'

Kerry put out her hand and held it against his cheek.

'You know him better even than I do. Oh, Steve, don't you see that I'm trying to tell you I love you. I only found out yesterday . . . when I heard you were going to marry someone else. I couldn't explain it to myself at first but I just knew that you couldn't, you mustn't, marry anyone but me! Then, when I heard your voice in the hall when you came in, I suddenly realized why. I wanted you for myself. I love you, Steve. I love you!'

He drew her into his arms, his face so

suffused with happiness and incredulity that it seemed to Kerry to be shining with a great light. She threw her arms round his neck and felt herself pressed against him fiercely, demandingly, until their two bodies seemed merged and she could no longer tell whether the heart beating was her own or his. Then his mouth came down to hers and the light that had been in Steve's eyes filled her body with such a sweet radiant joy, that she wondered briefly how it was possible that she had never realized it before.

Jo, coming into the room to announce lunch, stood and viewed them with a complacent contented smile on her face. She saw that they were unaware of her, impervious to thoughts of food or anything but each other. She watched them for a moment, a tiny voice of envy beating inside her for her own lost love. Then the smile returned. She went back into the kitchen, happily satisfied that at least for these two, their dreams were coming true.

She went to her handbag and searched until she found the paper she was looking for. It was a Deed of Sale for the cottage which she had bought when Steve put it on the market a few months ago. She touched it with a feeling of satisfaction that her instincts had been right after all.

'It'll make a nice wedding present!' she thought. 'And it'll be a wonderful surprise!'

She sat down at the table, happily thinking

of the future. There would be weekend visits, tea in the garden, winter evenings in front of the log fire. And later, there would be children and she would be a godmother. She remembered a poem by Thomas Lovell Beddoes.

> 'If there were dreams to sell
> What would you buy . . .
> Were dreams to have at will
> These would best heal my ill
> These would I buy.'

She waited another ten minutes and called them in to lunch.